Truth
DROPS

A SCRIPTURAL PROTOCOL FOR RELEASING
YOUR PAST WITH ESSENTIAL OILS

Stacy McDonald

ISBN: 978-1-7370846-3-1
Printed in the United States of America
First printing.

Growing Healthy Homes LLC
5701 SE Adams
Bartlesville, OK 74006

To obtain additional copies of this book, please visit
www.GrowingHealthyHomes.com.

All Scripture quotations, unless otherwise indicated, are taken from The Holy Bible, English Standard Version® (ESV®), copyright ©2001 by Crossway Bibles, a publishing ministry of Good News Publishers. Used by permission. All rights reserved.

Disclaimer: The author is not a mental health professional. The aromatherapy exercises, practices, prayers, essential oil suggestions, and information described in this book are for educational purposes only. They are not intended to prescribe, diagnose, or treat, any disease or condition.

This book is not intended to replace professional therapy or to diagnose or treat any mental health disorder as defined by The Diagnostic and Statistical Manual of Mental Disorders (DSM). If you believe you may have a mental disorder, please *seek the care of a qualified, mental health specialist.*

The content of this book does not necessarily reflect the views of *Young Living®* Essential Oils (YL), LLC, Lehi, UT, and is produced by a Brand Partner. All trademarks are used by permission.

The author, publisher, and YL bear no responsibility for the use or misuse of any of these products. The decision to use or not to use any of this information is the sole responsibility of the reader.

Dedication

The heart knoweth its own sorrow and there are times when, like David, it is comforting to think that our tears are put in a bottle and not one of them forgotten by the one who leads us in paths of sorrow.—Hannah Hurnard, *Hinds Feet on High Places*

Dedicated to the less-than child who fears that God has forgotten.

Acknowledgments

Thank you to my precious husband, James, the man who helped me to realize that I could be truly loved. Throughout the writing of this book, he gave me the encouragement and time to study, reflect, and heal. He prayed for me, kept the household running, and even developed new cooking skills (he became quite the chef in the process!). My darling, you are my greatest earthly love.

Thank you to my ten beautiful children (and their spouses) whose love, grace, and unwavering support throughout this process have been a healing balm. You and all your children—my cherished grandchildren—are my inspiration and greatest earthly treasure.

Thank you to my sweet friend, Tonya Chapa, my steadfast prayer partner, late-night encourager, and most trusted and faithful friend for the last two decades. Thank you for cheering me on!

Thank you to my brave friend, Crystal Sewell, whose friendship, encouragement, and personal experience with PTSD and trauma guided and boosted my decision to pursue therapy (which helped to give me the guts to write this book). You were a calming voice of reason when life got too loud.

Thank you to my strong friend, Lori Borre, whose years of partnership in life and business have been a cherished gift throughout our journey of faith, family, and oils. Hey Lori, "Look! We did it scared!"

Thank you to Mindy Mandel for her valuable input and proofing, as well as for our crucial brainstorming sessions!

Thank you to all my valued friends and family who gave me advice, proofed pages, offered encouraging words, and recommended books and oils. Though I dare not mention your names for fear of inadvertently leaving one of you out, you are not forgotten, and your contributions were essential to this work.

Thank you to our entire Common Scents Community, especially those who participated in our Freedom Class this past summer...you are my inspiration, and this is for you! Your stories, testimonies, personal development, and overall success have been a huge part of this project!

Thank you to my therapist, whose prayer, counsel, wisdom, compassion, and Scriptural focus helped me to unravel a lifetime of tangled perceptions. Thank you for always pointing me to Jesus.

Thank you to the late Dr. Gary Young and his wife, Mary, for their love, support, and ongoing commitment to the purity, quality, and integrity of God's gift of essential oils. Gary's expert formulations of the blends recommended in this book are part of what make Truth Drops such a powerful tool.

Thank you to my parents who, as a very young couple, shared in my trauma while attempting to heal from their own. Thank you for persevering through the confusing job of parenting a child with so many challenges. I love you.

Most of all, I am profoundly grateful to my Heavenly Father who loved, protected, and sustained me throughout the years...even when I knew Him not. I am not forsaken. Because of the sacrificial love of my Lord and Savior, Jesus Christ, I am forgiven and eternally secure in my Father's arms.

Thus says the Lord, who created you...and He who formed you... "Fear not, for I have redeemed you; I have called you by your name; you are Mine." (Isaiah 43:1)

Table of CONTENTS

About the AUTHOR

Christian author, blogger, and trauma survivor, Stacy McDonald, wrote this book while exploring her own troubled past. Though she had been a committed Christian for over thirty years, she still privately suffered from an unbiblical self-image and anxieties that she often struggled to control.

After seeking help from a licensed Christian therapist, she finally began to unravel and examine the irrational fears, painful memories, and unhealthy thought patterns that had become entrenched in her mind during her own difficult and complex childhood.

Maximizing the power of scent, Stacy took what she was learning about neuroplasticity (the brain's ability to change) and combined it with her knowledge and years of experience with essential oils and Scripture. From that, she created a unique and practical brain-training tool to enhance her own therapy process. Today, she shares this protocol with those needing to break free from the toxic thought patterns holding them back.

Preface

From where does my help come? My help comes from the Lord,
who made heaven and earth. (Psalm 121:1-2)

Can I tell you a little secret? For years, I coped with my anxiety by pretending it didn't exist, and by minimizing and ignoring things from my past that I preferred to forget. I'm just now, in my 50s, realizing the importance of dealing with it.

Deliberately applying the healing balm of God's Truth to the many lies my body has memorized and hidden is a process…. I'm still healing from a complex web of baggage and warped self-perceptions. One of the most significant motivating factors for writing this book is how insightful and therapeutic it has been for me. I needed to be accountable to do the hard work of sorting through my memories, reflecting on areas of dysfunction in my life, and making difficult changes. Writing, studying, and journaling have been a significant part of my overall progress.

We are all on a journey in this life, and it is my distinct privilege to provide you with this tool to use in your own healing journey—I hope it helps you as it has helped me. I'll walk with you through practical daily sessions I call Truth Drops—a simple daily protocol I created to help combat the lies in our head by bonding to the Truth of God's Word—His Living Word—Jesus.

The Word became flesh and dwelt among us... (John 1:14)

Throughout my time as a pastor's wife, numerous women came to me for help—women who struggled with rejection, shame, body image, abuse, bonding issues, abandonment, and more. Whether the trouble started from childhood, marital strife, an assault, or some other traumatic event, I discovered a common theme: Like me, most of these women had received lies about God and themselves—lies they believed and couldn't shake.

They believed the truth of God's Word, but they had trouble walking in its freedom. The lies were still hidden in the shadows of their soul. I had experienced the same struggle! In fact, looking back, at the time, I was completely unqualified to do much more than pray for these women. I was in the same boat.

It became clear to me that if we don't deliberately, consistently, and actively absorb the Truth, we will be vulnerable to manipulation, and we will inevitably consume at least traces of lies. And once we internalize a lie, it can get "stuck," even after we try to stop believing it.

Eventually, destructive thoughts can become addictive brain habits that replay when triggered by various life events. Instead of hiding God's Word in our hearts (Psalm 119:11), too often we allow lies to hide there—lies that became entrenched long ago.

You will know the truth, and the truth will set you free… if the Son sets you free, you will be free indeed. (John 8:32, 36)

After years of ministry, a decade of using and teaching about God's precious gift of essential oils, and during the process of my own professional therapy and healing with a Christian psychologist, I developed the exercises for *Truth Drops*.

While reading about neuroplasticity (the brain's ability to change), I decided to try using the influence of scent (essential oils) on the limbic system and link it to the power of God's Word to maximize the brain's own abilities.

I was learning about the effects of toxic thoughts on the mind; so, I decided to combine my knowledge of Scripture with my years of experience using essential oils. I created a unique and practical brain-training tool for those needing to break free from the toxic thought patterns holding them back.

I already knew essential oils had the remarkable ability to relax and soothe emotions. But, during sessions with my therapist, I noticed a marked improvement in productivity when I consistently applied and inhaled certain oils. Intrigued, I began to research the olfactory and limbic systems, which help to regulate emotion and memory.

I noticed that instead of being controlled by the lies in my head when triggered, if I used my oils, I found it easier to take every thought captive (2 Corinthians 10:5). This was so successful that I started to record and organize what I was doing.

Our sense of smell is so powerful that in a split second it can trigger a distant memory (and emotion) from childhood, which is why the scent of a familiar food, flower, or perfume can instantly transport us back emotionally to a specific scene from long ago.

The same thing happens the other way around (negatively) to people living with PTSD. But either way, there is no doubt that, because the amygdala responds instantly to the sense of smell[1], scent plays a significant part in forging memories. So why not let it work for us instead of against us?

CREATED FOR YOU AND ME

There are 1,031 references to essential oils, aromatic oil-producing plants, and their applications in the Bible, including at least 33 species.—Dr. David Stewart, *Healing Oils of the Bible*

I contemplated how often and how many fragrant oils were famously mentioned throughout the Holy Scriptures. Essential oils were used in ancient times for worship, cleansing, and healing. Precious Frankincense and Myrrh, as well as gold, were given by the Wise Men as treasured gifts to Jesus at His birth.

Essential oils were used to anoint the sick, perfume beds, and for appointing kings. Again, like gold, essential oils were highly valued!

---

1   Dr. Benjamin Perkus, *The Aroma Freedom Technique* p.11.

Is anyone among you sick? Let him call for the elders of the church, and let them pray over him, anointing him with oil in the name of the Lord. (James 5:14)

Knowing what I know about now-endangered (and unavailable) Spikenard, and realizing that this was the precious essential oil selected and poured on the head and feet of Jesus (Mark 14:3, John 12:3), it hit me.

Spikenard is one of the most intensely relaxing essential oils God ever created. It's actually in the same family as Valerian. Valerian is well known for helping ease stressful moments. Can you imagine anything more intense and stressful than the unspeakable suffering Jesus was about to endure on the cross?

Jesus was fully God and fully man. Jesus lovingly acknowledged her efforts as an act of compassion and worship before His crucifixion. Jesus even said she had come to anoint him for burial (Mark 14:8)!

Since our minds and bodies are fearfully and wonderfully made by a loving Creator who provides for our every need, and because of the way the olfactory system works within the limbic system, we can enlist the help of essential oils to work through past hurts and to deliberately forge new, healthy thought patterns—or "brain habits." Inhale the truth; exhale the lies.

CHANGING THE SCENT OF DANGER

Each Truth Drop Session walks you through aroma-filled, brain-training exercises using different essential oils, faith-based affirmations, and Scripture. It is my hope that you will evaluate your own emotional responses, gain new perspectives on your past, reject false perceptions, and develop healthier responses by building new pathways in the brain.

The power of scent and your own limbic system has the potential to ease your journey through the past and link it to the real and present truth of God's Word (John 8:32), offering you a fresh, healthy perspective on the future!

Consistently replace the lies you may have absorbed with powerful Scripture-backed "Truth Affirmations," as well as "Affirmation Supports" (corresponding Scripture verses), to confirm with certainty each affirmation in your mind. Confess God's opinion as supreme.

Unlike the popular practice of repeating "positive affirmations" (which, as helpful as they are, could be made-up words in our head), Truth Drops don't involve wishful thinking. When I speak the Truth Affirmations in this book and back them up with the verses that support them, *I know* that God's Word is always true!

As I've consistently incorporated this life-changing practice into my healing journey, I've felt much more in tune with my emotions and in control of the negative responses that had been frantically working behind the scenes in the story of my life.

I believe He wants to do the same for you! These exercises are powerful because greater is He who is within us than he who is in the world (1 John 4:4). Jesus has the power to change *everything!*

The oil of gladness instead of mourning… (Isaiah 61:3)

INTRODUCTION

Brain Habits: God's Gift of Neuroplasticity

God doesn't lie, so when His Word says that He "heals the brokenhearted" (Psalm 147:3), we can and should believe it; and because He created us as physical, emotional, and spiritual beings, He cares about our *emotional* health as much as He cares about our physical and spiritual needs. He loves His children, and He wants us to be whole.

By employing the "super-power" of our own limbic/olfactory system, we can use essential oils to train our brain to automatically respond by neurologically linking the soothing aromas of God's gift of plants with what He says about us in His Word (Ezekiel 47:12).

The goal is to establish a thought-scent association that will rewire neural pathways, creating healthy, rather than toxic, response patterns. This new pathway, once established, demonstrates what scientists call *neuroplasticity*.

> *Do not be conformed to this world, but be transformed by the renewing of your mind, that you may prove what is that good and acceptable and perfect will of God.* (Romans 12:2)

Whether it's nail biting, cracking your knuckles, or the consistent use of the word "um," most of us have at least some sort of persistent brain habit we can't seem to shake. Some habits are more problematic than others. Likewise, most of us establish and create healthy habits that serve us well.

*Your brain forms neuronal connections based on what you do repeatedly in your life—both good and bad. Worrying about every little thing. Cruising online pornography. Picking at your fingernails. Hitting the gym. Meditating. Your repeated mental states, ways of responding, and behaviors become neural traits.—*thebestbrainpossible.com

Neuroplasticity displays your brain's amazing ability to physically change based on the emotions you memorize throughout the positive and negative experiences in your life, as well as your repeated behaviors and thoughts. This can be either dangerous or empowering, depending upon how deliberate you are with the potential effects of this remarkable ability.

ADDICTIONS AND BAD HABITS

Renewing the mind isn't pie-in-the-sky impossible; it's a real thing. And, as a Believer, it's for *you*. To renew the mind, we begin by making a conscious decision to *believe* the truth about what God says in His Word and then *practicing* it. It's a decision made first in the mind, but by acting on it—by doing it, and by doing it regularly—we begin to "practice" it. And practice makes perfect…well, perfect-*ing*! That's what training is all about. Good or bad, habits are formed.

When we practice something long enough, it becomes automatic. We don't have to think about it—we just do it without concentrating on the details. When a pianist is playing, she doesn't think about where her fingers should go … they just glide over the keys—implicit muscle memory. When someone passes the salt at the table, you may automatically say "thank you" without a thought. When you sign your name, you no longer have to think about the shape or order of the letters, and there is no need to concentrate on how to hold your pen. After enough practice, these things just come naturally. In fact, sometimes thinking about things too much may even throw you off.

Consistently training your brain until a thought is automatic can help you create new brain habits and internalize the truth of who you are in God's eyes. If you are deliberate in this activity, you can acknowledge and release hurts more efficiently, and you will develop healthier thought patterns and a more accurate perception of yourself and your past.

Although I have designed these sessions for you to do every morning and every evening for nine consecutive weeks, feel free, during difficult moments in your day, to repeat any of these exercises as many times as necessary. This practice will help you to leverage the power of God's Word to "renew your mind" (Romans 12:2) and "take every thought captive" (2 Corinthians 10:5).

PURITY MATTERS

For these sessions, I can't stress enough how important it is to use only pure essential oils that are of the highest quality and efficacy. You want oils that *work*. Most oils you find on the shelves in stores are produced for the cleaning, candle, and perfume industry, so they are low quality. Their purpose is only to smell good.

A large number even contain toxic solvents, pesticides, chemical extenders, or synthetic fragrances that could have damaging effects to our bodies. See my *Guide to Choosing Quality Essential Oils* in the Appendix for details on how to evaluate oils to find those that are safe and effective.

God gave us an amazing gift when He blessed us with essential oils. Adam and Eve enjoyed a beautiful and fragrant existence in the Garden of Eden, surrounded by the therapeutic aromas of the hundreds of plants, trees, flowers, and shrubs contained there.

Regardless of whether you like essential oils or not, I urge you to give them a try. Remember, our goal is to retrain or rewire our brains with new neural pathways (thinking habits) so that, when memories are triggered, we can view and manage our thoughts in a more productive and healthy way.

As you go through each session, speak the affirmations and supporting verses aloud, take your time to enjoy the healing aroma of each oil, and ponder and memorize the experience of each individual truth you're focusing on, deliberately associating the aroma in your mind. Even if you don't initially love the scent of a particular oil, you will likely find that, over time, your perception of the aroma will begin to transform, as you associate it with the sweetness of God's Word.

Don't be surprised if an oil you at first disliked suddenly transforms into your very favorite scent. I can't count the number of times this has happened to me! Let the oil work as you speak God's Word over yourself and internalize its truth. Your deliberate, new thoughts will be backed up by the truth of God's Word and reinforced using the natural design of your God-given limbic system.

According to the late Dr. David Stewart, author of *Healing Oils of the Bible*, oils high in phenylpropanoids clean receptor sites, sesquiterpenes "delete" garbled information stored in cellular memory, and monoterpenes "reprogram" them, so that they can function properly.[2] Fascinating stuff! Imagine the potential. Since smell and memory are linked so directly, the possibilities appear to be endless. Clinical Psychologist Dr. Benjamin Perkus claims to use essential oils in his therapy practice with great results:

> *In using essential oils to assist with processing of stressful memories, I was struck by how there seemed to be a spontaneous realignment of images, feelings, and belief systems as people smelled the oils while in a particular phase of the release process. There seems to be a deep connection between the sense of smell and memory, and we were somehow changing the meaning of these memories by introducing the oils at the right time.*—Dr. Benjamin Perkus[3]

This is encouraging, as many researchers believe trauma and anxiety alter our DNA and can be passed down to future generations through epigenesis.[4] Have you ever noticed how certain habits seem to be present over several generations, such as nail-biting, a nervous tick, or even a propensity for substance abuse?

Not all behaviors are learned; some may be passed down genetically. And, although each of us is responsible for our own actions, even a proclivity for certain sins can be passed down throughout the generations (Deuteronomy 5:9). Thankfully, God also *blesses* future generations (Deuteronomy 7:9). So, the change can start with us, today.

---

2   Stewart, D. (2007). *Healing Oils of the Bible.* 1st ed. Marble Hill, MO, Care Publications.
3   Dr. Perkus, B. (2017). *The Aroma Freedom Technique,* 2nd ed. Binghamton, NY, Aroma Freedom International.
4   https://www.scientificamerican.com/article/fearful-memories-passed-down/

THE FIVE SENSES

Besides our sense of smell, which is the focus of this book, leveraging our other God-given senses can be helpful during therapy, too. For instance, meditative music or the sound of trickling water can be relaxing. Soaking in a soothing, warm tub; lying in soft, green grass; holding hands with someone we love; cuddling a baby; or even hugging a friend can satisfy our need for physical touch.

What we see with our eyes is also part of our well-being, which is why tranquil scenery, soft lighting, and specific colors can be very soothing to the soul. Be mindful of this while you go through the sessions in this book and choose surroundings that will complement your experience.

Most importantly, in order to create a consistent practice of renewing your mind each day, set aside a special time of silence, solitude, and prayer. Jesus set this example for us throughout His ministry on earth, even in the midst of busyness and opposition:

Now in the morning, having risen a long while before daylight, He went out and departed to a solitary place; and there He prayed. (Mark 1:35)

In these days He went out to the mountain to pray, and all night He continued in prayer to God. (Luke 6:12)

God has armed our bodies with intricate ways to heal from the fiery darts the world throws at us. He provides for our every need, and He will not leave us unequipped for whatever He calls us to do. He has given us stewardship over the earth for a divine purpose—to bring Him glory through love and service to others.

Isn't it a comfort to know that, at Creation, when Jehovah Jireh ("God our Provider") made the plants and trees, and even that very first flower, He had our well-being in mind? He lovingly infused each drop of essential oil with great potential when He spoke into existence the myriad of plants and trees. He hid precious oils inside of each aromatic, living plant He crafted, and within each one, He placed a multitude of powerful, complex constituents. The Bible says in Psalm 104 that He created the plants "for the service of man."

I will praise You, for I am fearfully and wonderfully made; marvelous are Your works, and that my soul knows very well. (Psalm 139:14, NKJV)

God intended for them to be enjoyable and valuable gifts (James 1:17) for us to treasure. And, as we are fearfully and wonderfully made, our bodies are created to work in harmony with nature to deal with the many shadows of life (Ezekiel 47:12).

VOODOO OILS

To be clear, there is nothing mystical about essential oils, and when a Christian uses them during prayer, they are not using something "New Age" or intrinsically spiritual. Essential oils are God's precious gift to man—part of His amazing Creation. Science and Scripture repeatedly back this up.

Using a drop of essential oil during prayer and meditation would not be much different than tearing the leaves of any aromatic plant and rubbing them in your hands to inhale and enjoy. Today, modern Christians too often throw the baby out with the bath water. We need to stop inadvertently relinquishing our rights to God's good gift of natural health—and utilize these precious resources that encourage the body to do what He designed it to do!

THE GREAT PHYSICIAN

Without faith it is impossible to please Him, for whoever would draw near to God must believe that he exists and that He rewards those who seek Him. (Hebrews 11:6)

God is our ultimate Provider. In Genesis 22:14, He is called Jehovah Jireh, which is Hebrew for "the Lord will provide." He is also called Jehovah Rapha, which means God is our healer. When we sing the doxology, we "praise God from whom all blessings flow." In James 1:17 we're reminded that "every good gift and every perfect gift is from above."

Even when we need to seek help from a doctor or surgeon, we must remember that the Great Physician is ultimately in control of all healing.

Is anyone among you sick? Let him call for the elders of the church, and let them pray over him, anointing him with oil in the name of the Lord. And the prayer of faith will save the sick, and the Lord will raise him up… (James 5:14-15)

We cannot simultaneously embrace both fear and faith; so, make sure you bond with the One who has the power to transform your fear *into* faith. He changes *everything*.

His Son, Jesus, is the only One who can offer you true and lasting change. You can convince yourself of a lot of things using positive affirmations and persuasive speech, but without Jesus, the Truth of His Word, and the power of His healing touch, overcoming the toxic effects from your past will be limited.

You will seek Me and find Me, when you search for Me with all your heart. (Jeremiah 29:13, NKJV)

WHAT IF I'M NOT "RELIGIOUS?"

If you have never met the God of the Universe, you may think all of this sounds impossible. You might be asking yourself how you can have faith in a God you've never even known. He already knows *you*, and He knows your heart. If you are willing, cry out to Him the way the father of the demon-possessed boy did in Mark 9:24, "Lord, I believe; help my unbelief!" He sees, and He is faithful!

I have named you, though you have not known Me… (Isaiah 45:2, NKJV)

Regardless of whether you are simply hoping to change simple, negative thinking patterns or you have experienced deep trauma, betrayal, rejection, or worse in your past, God can help you achieve lasting emotional and spiritual healing. Without Him, we are empty; and we can't know genuine peace.

As we walk together through the sessions in this book, and you learn to internalize the truth found in God's Word, my prayer is that you will begin to see yourself the way Jesus sees you—as a cherished, precious soul made in His very image. As you infuse God's Word into your mind and spirit, I pray you put your full trust in Him and develop a stronger, healthier, and more intimate bond with our loving Creator and with others.

How to Practice Truth Drops

We have to recognize and accept that when it comes to the mind, there really are no quick fixes. Trying to make things happen fast can cause unnecessary anguish and put your brain and body into toxic stress, keeping you stuck in the addiction cycle.—Dr. Caroline Leaf, *Switch on Your Brain*

Dr. Leaf[5] says "it takes 21 days to start changing neural pathways," and that "it takes a minimum of 63 days to build or change an existing thinking habit, while most people tend to give up around day four!" The sessions in this book are designed to maximize this concept by walking you through nine weeks of Truth Drops—63 days of consistent brain training, pursuing the goal of "renewing the mind" and "taking every thought captive." (Romans 12:2, 2 Corinthians 10:5)

The essential oil suggestions on the following pages and in the Appendix are designed to assist you in your selection of six oils (one Prayer Oil and five Affirmation Oils). Use these oils consistently and in the same order as directed every morning and evening while going through your Truth Drop Sessions each week for the full nine weeks.

You may find it helpful to set your selected oils out together on a special tray on your desk or kitchen counter. That way, they're easily visible and accessible during your daily routine (or if needed more often). Remember, consistency matters in brain training!

---

5   https://drleaf.com/blogs/news

BEGIN WITH PRAYER

At the beginning of each session, I will guide you through a starter prayer. Use the Prayer Oil you selected to anoint yourself as explained below before you pray. Do this as confirmation to the Lord and to yourself that you are relying on Him and His Word, not simply on your own strength.

Be sure to personalize your time with the Lord by sharing your heart with Him: Tell Him your needs, ask Him for help, and offer Him your genuine expressions of praise and gratitude. Also, ask him to search your heart and reveal hidden areas He wants to heal.

As you pray, ask Him questions, and wait expectantly for answers. Have a journal ready to record your impressions and experiences. Your interaction with God is not one-sided. Deliberately pursue and build a thriving, interactive relationship with Him.

I also like to put a drop of my selected Prayer Oil on one of the pages of my Bible, so that when I'm in God's Word, the scent automatically transports me into a mental posture of prayer (this is more powerful than you think). Plus, it's a great reminder that we are to be the fragrant aroma of Christ to others.

> *Thanks be to God who always leads us in triumph in Christ, and through us diffuses the fragrance of His knowledge in every place. For we are to God the fragrance of Christ among those who are being saved and among those who are perishing...* (2 Corinthians 2:14, NKJV)

As you begin each session, anoint yourself by placing 1-3 drops of your selected Prayer Oil into the palm of one hand. Swirl a finger from your other hand into the oil in your palm and use it to apply the oil across your forehead, near your hairline, back and forth several times.

Using one finger, drag the oil to your left temple and rub in a circular, clockwise motion. Then drag it across your forehead to your right temple and repeat the same circular motion.[6]

---

6   Some experts claim the brain does its best emotional shifting from left to right and in a clockwise direction. While I can't find scientific evidence to prove this theory, I know many people who insist this practice has made a difference for them.

Rub your hands together (using more oil if necessary), cup your hands over your face, and deeply inhale the residual oil. Pause, and very slowly, exhale through your mouth. Relax, breathe again, and mindfully enjoy the aroma as you pray.

Make it your practice to go through the Truth Drops consistently as I've outlined in each session. Each week of the nine Truth Drop Sessions has its own unique topic, but the same six oils will be used for the entire nine weeks.

TRUTH AFFIRMATIONS

After your prayer time, repeat the process of anointing and breathing, by applying and inhaling each of your five chosen Affirmation Oils according to the instructions in each exercise. It's very important to speak your affirmations and support Scripture out loud. Speaking your truth—as well as God's Word—over yourself is a great way to rewire your brain while taking God's Word into your heart (and into your neurological system!).

This book contains nine Truth Drop Sessions. Each contains:
- A Starter Prayer
- Five Truth Affirmations
- Three Affirmation Supports (Scripture verses) to back up each affirmation
- A Journal Prompt

TRUTH DROP "BUNDLES"

On the following pages, as well as in the Appendix at the back of this book, you will find suggestions for which essential oils to use during your Truth Drop Sessions. I've listed oils I have personally used and found to be emotionally beneficial. I also included those I selected after researching which singles and blends[7] are the most effective for overall emotional support.

---

7   Over a decade ago, after researching and trying other brands, I found that Young Living® Essential Oils were the only oils that met my personal standards for purity and efficacy. So, I designed these exercises to be practiced only with Young Living essential oils. For that reason, the blends mentioned in this book refer to these expertly formulated proprietary blends.

However, because everyone's biological and psychological makeup is different, and because there are so many good choices, I don't want to overwhelm you by listing them all. So, to make it easy for you to jump right in, I've included several oil bundles for you to choose from. Each bundle contains the necessary combination of one Prayer Oil and five Affirmation Oils. But please feel free to personalize your choices and use whichever combination best fits your needs. The complete list of recommended oils and blends for this book can be found in the Appendix. The key is to be consistent with your choices over the next 63 days. This will help you to reinforce new thoughts and turn them into automatic "brain habits."

Choose One Truth Drop Bundle or Create Your Own!

RESTORATION BUNDLE
I will restore to you the years that the swarming locust has eaten. (Joel 2:25)
    Chosen Prayer Oil: Frankincense
    Chosen Affirmation Oil #1: Inner Child™
    Chosen Affirmation Oil #2: SARA™
    Chosen Affirmation Oil #3: Petitgrain
    Chosen Affirmation Oil #4: Release™
    Chosen Affirmation Oil #5: Highest Potential™

CONFIDENCE BUNDLE
Let us then with confidence draw near to the throne of grace… (Hebrews 4:16)
    Chosen Prayer Oil: Sacred Sandalwood (Aloes)
    Chosen Affirmation Oil #1: Motivation™
    Chosen Affirmation Oil #2: Petitgrain
    Chosen Affirmation Oil #3: Gratitude™
    Chosen Affirmation Oil #4: Neroli
    Chosen Affirmation Oil #5: Valor®

BODY IMAGE BUNDLE
I am fearfully and wonderfully made. Wonderful are Your works… (Psalm 139:14)
    Chosen Prayer Oil: Rose of Sharon (Cistus)
    Chosen Affirmation Oil #1: Vetiver
    Chosen Affirmation Oil #2: Gratitude™
    Chosen Affirmation Oil #3: Petitgrain
    Chosen Affirmation Oil #4: White Angelica™
    Chosen Affirmation Oil #5: Abundance™

SHAME BUNDLE
You will forget the shame of your youth... (Isaiah 54:4)
    Chosen Prayer Oil: Hyssop
    Chosen Affirmation Oil #1: Inner Child™
    Chosen Affirmation Oil #2: Sacred Mountain™
    Chosen Affirmation Oil #3: SARA™
    Chosen Affirmation Oil #4: Release™
    Chosen Affirmation Oil #5: Neroli

INNER JOY BUNDLE
Everlasting joy shall be upon their heads...sorrow and sighing shall flee away.
(Isaiah 35:10)
    Chosen Prayer Oil: Onycha
    Chosen Affirmation Oil #1: Sacred Mountain™
    Chosen Affirmation Oil #2: Present Time™
    Chosen Affirmation Oil #3: Tranquil™
    Chosen Affirmation Oil #4: Hope™
    Chosen Affirmation Oil #5: Joy™

GLADNESS BUNDLE
The oil of gladness instead of mourning... (Isaiah 61:3)
    Chosen Prayer Oil: Frankincense
    Chosen Affirmation Oil #1: Orange
    Chosen Affirmation Oil #2: One Voice™
    Chosen Affirmation Oil #3: Peace & Calming™
    Chosen Affirmation Oil #4: Lavender
    Chosen Affirmation Oil #5: Joy™

FORGIVENESS BUNDLE
If the Son makes you free, you shall be free indeed. (John 8:36)
    Chosen Prayer Oil: Sacred Sandalwood
    Chosen Affirmation Oil #1: Inner Child™
    Chosen Affirmation Oil #2: Trauma life™
    Chosen Affirmation Oil #3: Forgiveness™
    Chosen Affirmation Oil #4: Surrender™
    Chosen Affirmation Oil #5: Release™

CONSOLATION & COMFORT BUNDLE

To console those who mourn in Zion, to give them beauty for ashes, the oil of joy for mourning, the garment of praise for the spirit of heaviness... (Isaiah 61:3, NKJV)

Chosen Prayer Oil: Rose of Sharon (Cistus)
Chosen Affirmation Oil #1: Present Time™
Chosen Affirmation Oil #2: Hope™
Chosen Affirmation Oil #3: Neroli
Chosen Affirmation Oil #4: Gratitude™
Chosen Affirmation Oil #5: Joy™

ABUNDANCE BUNDLE

But the meek shall inherit the earth, and shall delight themselves in the abundance of peace. (Psalm 37:11)

Chosen Prayer Oil: Frankincense
Chosen Affirmation Oil #1: Motivation™
Chosen Affirmation Oil #2: Envision™
Chosen Affirmation Oil #3: Magnify Your Purpose™
Chosen Affirmation Oil #4: Highest Potential ™
Chosen Affirmation Oil #5: Abundance™

ASSURANCE BUNDLE

I have come that they may have life, and that they may have it more abundantly. (John 10:10)

Chosen Prayer Oil: Cedarwood
Chosen Affirmation Oil #1: Believe™
Chosen Affirmation Oil #2: Petitgrain
Chosen Affirmation Oil #3: Hope™
Chosen Affirmation Oil #4: Gathering™
Chosen Affirmation Oil #5: Valor®

CONNECTION BUNDLE

Two are better than one... (Ecclesiastes 4:9)

Chosen Prayer Oil: Myrtle
Chosen Affirmation Oil #1: Gathering™
Chosen Affirmation Oil #2: Black Pepper
Chosen Affirmation Oil #3: Sensation™
Chosen Affirmation Oil #4: Transformation™
Chosen Affirmation Oil #5: Awaken™

Whichever bundle you choose or create, be sure to use the same oil combination for the full nine weeks. However, when necessary, you may switch to a new bundle at the 30-day mark. This is particularly necessary if you are using the *Freedom Sleep™* and *Release™ Collection[8]:*

FREEDOM BUNDLE[9]
He has sent me to proclaim liberty to the captives and recovering of sight to the blind, to set at liberty those who are oppressed. (Luke 4:18)

Freedom Sleep
Weeks 1-5
 Chosen Prayer Oil: Frankincense
 Chosen Affirmation Oil #1: Freedom™
 Chosen Affirmation Oil #2: AromaSleep™
 Chosen Affirmation Oil #3: Valor®
 Chosen Affirmation Oil #4: Inner Harmony™
 Chosen Affirmation Oil #5: Cedarwood

Freedom Release
Weeks 6-9
 Chosen Prayer Oil: Frankincense
 Chosen Affirmation Oil #1: Freedom™
 Chosen Affirmation Oil #2: Joy™
 Chosen Affirmation Oil #3: Transformation™
 Chosen Affirmation Oil #4: Divine Release™
 Chosen Affirmation Oil #5: T.R. Care™

INHALE THE TRUTH AND EXHALE THE LIES!

God's healing power can help you to feel and gently grieve the loss of all that could or should have been and then release the destructive thought patterns and memories that have harmed your success and held you back in life.

---

8   Young Living's Freedom Sleep™ and Release™ Collection comes with its own unique application instructions.
9   All but two of the oils in the Freedom Bundle (Frankincense and Cedarwood) are included in the Freedom Sleep™ and Release™ Collection sold as a set by Young Living®.

Using neuroplasticity to maximize the natural function of my limbic system is teaching my brain to automatically respond by associating the aromas of powerful essential oils with what God says about me in His Word. This approach has been extremely productive, gentle, and healing for me, and I believe that God can use it to do the same for you.

Their fruit will be for food, and their leaves for healing... (Ezekiel 47:12)

I invite you to join me in using this powerful tool! As you acknowledge and release hurts, create healthier brain habits, and internalize the truth about who you are in God's eyes, you will see change. I believe this practice will lead you to healthier thought patterns and a more accurate perception of yourself and your past.

Remember, depending on your personal history or situation, you may find yourself working through some heavy topics; so, be prepared for the possibility that strong or raw emotions may arise at times. If necessary, seek the help of a trusted counselor or qualified professional Christian therapist to walk you through this process.

Take the time to pray through each step of your journey, meditate on God's Word, and be open to what He wants to do in your heart and mind. As you work through *Truth Drops*, learn to not waste the pain in your life. Feel it, push into it, and make it work *for* you. God can use every drop of it to transform and renew your mind. Remember, inhale the truth; exhale the lies!

Whether you are dealing with past trauma or abuse, or you simply want to change a bad habit of toxic thinking, there is hope. The time has come for healing and breaking free from what has kept you "stuck." I invite you to join me on this personal journey. So, oil up, pray up, face the truth, and break free of toxic emotional patterns—I'm cheering for you!

For the weapons of our warfare are not of the flesh but
have divine power to destroy strongholds... and take every thought
captive to obey Christ... (2 Corinthians 10:4-5)

CHAPTER 1

The Less-Than Girl

From my mother's womb
You have chosen me
Love has called my name
I've been born again
Into your family
Your blood flows though my veins.
—Zach Williams, *Bethel Music*

I was born to a teen mom entangled in the "free-love" culture of the '60s. Ironically, that sort of love turned out to be anything but free. Because of the social stigmas of the day, and to avoid scandal, my birthmother was sent away for the last three months of her pregnancy to give birth to me in secret. Even her grandparents and six younger siblings didn't know I existed until our reunion 21 years later.

My late paternal grandfather, Dr. Michael DeBakey, worked as a cardiovascular surgeon in the Houston hospital where I was born. During that same year, he performed the first-ever successful implantation of the left ventricular bypass pump, which he developed.

My grandfather was at the height of his career and fame during my birthmother's pregnancy, so if the press had been made aware of my existence, there would have been a public scandal. This may be one reason why my birthmother's pregnancy was kept secret, even from family.

At my birth, after the doctors discovered I had Spina Bifida, they informed my birth family that, even if I lived, they didn't expect me to ever walk. They also warned my grandparents that my medical expenses (which wound up including several major surgeries and extensive bracing) would be staggering—daunting words for an already traumatized family.

The first couple who had planned to adopt me backed out when they discovered I had a "birth defect." Even years after I was born, some babies with Spina Bifida were assessed using a certain quality-of-life formula: $QL=NE \times (HS)$[10] and were left to die untreated in hospitals to spare them an unfit existence.[11]

> *For my father and my mother have forsaken me,*
> *but the Lord will take me in.* (Psalm 27:10)

After being left in the care of rotating hospital nurses for at least the first three months of my life, I was eventually placed in foster care and lived with a family who spoke only Spanish. For two years, my birthmother refused to sign the adoption papers, holding out hope that she could finish high school and find a way to get me back.

My birthmother graduated high school in 1968 and approached her parents one last time, hoping for help to regain custody of me. However, they ultimately convinced her that it was in my best interest, as well as her own, to pursue a nursing degree instead. The consensus was that I would be better off with a responsible couple who could give me what she couldn't provide—a financially stable home with married parents.

ADOPTION

After my birthmother reluctantly signed the adoption papers in 1968, I was officially placed with a young couple who was still grieving the tragic death of their own infant daughter during childbirth.

The birthing experience had been very traumatic for my adoptive mother. She awoke from anesthesia alone and confused, unaware that her daughter had died until a nurse finally came in to inform her. She

---

10   "QL stands for quality of life, NE represents the patient's natural endowment, both physical and intellectual, H is the emotional and financial contribution from home and family, and S is the financial contribution from society."

11   https://www.oklahoman.com/article/2123212/spina-bifida-lawsuit-filed

was never even able to hold her baby and was so distressed over the whole experience that she spiraled into a depression. For months, she was inconsolable. So, when my parents saw a notice from Catholic Charities posted in their church bulletin about a little girl who needed a home, they viewed it as providential. My father said he had hoped that adopting me would help heal my mother's depression.

My birthmother with her little brother, months before I was born in 1966.

I later discovered that just a few years after I was adopted, on Mother's Day 1971, my birthmother's life ended in tragedy at the tender age of 21. I never had the chance to know her, but only months after my own 21st birthday, in 1987, I was reunited with her large, close-knit family, as well as my birthfather, my half-sister, and two of my uncles. Most of my family hadn't known I existed before that time.

Adoption Day—Houston Zoo 1968

After I was adopted, those early years were hard. Not much was known back then about attachment theory, trauma, or the complexities of mother-infant bonding, and there wasn't any such thing as adoption support groups or that type of specialized counseling.

My adoptive mother became pregnant again about a year after they adopted me. I faintly remember when she came home from the hospital with my newborn sister. While I was thrilled to have a sister, I yearned intensely for the same closeness I observed between the two of them, and I recall the distinct feeling that I was somehow "different."

It wasn't long after my sister was born that I began to believe my parents were "stuck" with me—I felt ugly and defective. I longed to feel genuinely wanted—to be cherished rather than tolerated.

(far left) My sister and me—1972

I sometimes overheard my parents' friends, when discussing the fact that I was adopted, congratulate my parents for their kindness. This made me feel strangely shamed and indebted. I didn't want to be someone's good deed. The words from their good-intentioned friends made me feel like a burden. I often chided myself for not being grateful enough.

Throughout my childhood, between painful, humiliating medical procedures, years of relentless bullying at school for merely existing, and regular reminders that I wasn't enough, life was full of physical and emotional stress. Whether at home or school, it felt like I couldn't do anything right. It seemed the slightest wrong move would result in some sort of trouble or disapproval. Rejection lurked around every corner.

THE BRACE

I was in the first grade when my "metal years" began. For seven years, and in the brutal heat and humidity of Houston, Texas, I wore a large, heavy, metal back brace 24/7 (a Milwaukee Back Brace).

I felt trapped behind all that metal, and the collar of the brace choked me. It was stifling hot under the heavy encasement around my hips, where sweat became trapped and made my skin sore and itchy. My hair often became tangled in the screws behind my neck and the front screw on the left side of the brace was situated right in front of my breast and protruded awkwardly. This made puberty just SUPER fun in public school.

As I got older, my mom did the best she could to help me hide my brace, but the metal constantly ripped through my clothing and kept me from wearing stretchy cotton or any sort of stylish clothing that fit properly.

Underneath the brace, I wore a tube-shaped "stocking" to absorb excess moisture and help with skin protection. But sometimes, the pressure sores on my hips oozed, then they dried and stuck to the cloth, so the newly forming scabs had to be ripped off at the end of the day. Then, after replacing the old stocking with a fresh one, I still had to put the brace back on before bed.

I also had to wear a clunky shoe lift because my left leg was an inch and a half shorter than my right. I frequently injured that foot (we called it my "monster foot") due to semi-paralysis related to the Spina Bifida. Even though I have no feeling in that foot, I still can't stand for anyone to look at or touch it.

PUBLIC SCHOOL

Public school was a nightmare of taunting, fear, and public shaming. When I was about eight years old, I asked my mother what an erector set was. After she told me, I understood the meaning of my new nickname. By junior high, it had become worse. "Hey, Brace-butt, do you have a metal bra to go with your metal body?"

In 6th and 7th grade, I was frequently followed home from the bus stop by kids mocking and throwing things at me. Boys trailed behind me, whispering and making sexual comments, while the girls spat at me and laughed, calling me weird and ugly. I cried as one boy followed behind me, randomly poking me in the backside with his umbrella and laughing.

Be gracious to me, O Lord, for I am languishing; heal me, O Lord, for my bones are troubled. My soul also is greatly troubled. But you, O Lord—how long? (Psalm 6:2-3)

Humiliation seemed to follow me everywhere. While I was in the hospital for my spinal fusion (at 12 or 13), I was required to stand in nothing but my underwear with my back facing a panel of male student-doctors. It was in an arena-style hospital classroom, and I was center-stage. They asked me to bend over in various positions to better evaluate and discuss the curve in my spine. Someone else was taking medical photos. I still recall the repeated flash of the camera.

Early on, I learned how to sob silently into my pillow at night—mastering the art of "quiet crying"—internalizing the explosive grief I felt. After exhausting myself, I just turned over my pillow, so I didn't have to sleep in the wet spot.

I screamed inside my head all the things I wasn't allowed to say out loud. When chastised, I managed to hold my breath and blink back tears while my mind cried in agony. I closed my eyes and made the world go away. I figured out how to please the people who mattered to me and avoid those who felt like a threat. I learned how to *survive*.

In my bed at night, I held long, silent conversations with myself (and sometimes with God), agonizing over how ugly, stupid, and worthless I was. I went through my ever-growing mental checklist of everything that was "wrong" with me. I cried bitter tears. Years later, I eventually found it difficult to cry at all.

> *O Lord, why do you cast my soul away? Why do You hide Your face from me? Afflicted and close to death from my youth up, I suffer Your terrors; I am helpless...* (Psalm 88:14-15)

I just knew that I somehow deserved what I was going through, but I didn't know why or how to fix it or make it all stop. Sometimes I asked God, "Please, please let me die." I contemplated suicide many times, but I was terrified I would get that wrong, too, and I'd wake up worse off, paralyzed in a hospital somewhere, and in even more trouble—or maybe in Hell.

> *I am weary with my moaning; every night I flood my bed with tears; I drench my couch with my weeping. My eye wastes away because of grief; it grows weak because of all my foes.* (Psalm 6:6-7)

By dwelling on all that was wrong with me and how much I was hated through these obsessive, daily mental exercises, I forged chains that kept me in a secret, self-created, self-regulated torture chamber for years. It was a bondage even more traumatizing than my back brace; it permeated every part of my life and influenced the many poor choices

I made along the way. If it hadn't been for a loving God who delights in extending extravagant mercy, I would never have survived it.

My frame was not hidden from you, when I was being made in secret, intricately woven... (Psalm 139:15)

A LIGHT AT THE END OF THE TUNNEL...OR IS THAT A TRAIN?

Somewhere along the way, I began to hope that my big problem was the back brace I wore. "If it weren't for the brace, I could be like everyone else, and people would like me." I temporarily made my brace the scapegoat and blamed it for all the pain in my life. I started fantasizing about my approaching day of emancipation—surgery day—the day I would finally be rid of the brace that made people hate me!

The summer before my 13th birthday, the day came—the day of my last major back surgery, which would fuse my spine for good and keep my lungs from being further compromised. I was to spend nine months in a body cast following the operation, but after that I would finally be rid of the thing that made me an outcast—that made me unlovable.

Though the two-week hospital stay was painful and came with its own traumatic moments (a male nurse should never sponge-bathe a pubescent young girl), I was still optimistic. I looked forward to my nightmare being over. Soon, I would be free!

When the nine-month-casting was up, the heavy plaster was finally removed. I was thrilled! I was glad to go through all of it in exchange for my eagerly awaited new identity as a "normal kid."

But the day came and went; and, unlike Cinderella, no fairy godmother transformed me from rags and ashes into a beautiful, brace-free princess. The godmother had come and gone, the clock had struck midnight, and I was still the same old less-than girl I'd always been.

This confirmed in my mind that it wasn't the brace that had made me unlovable. It was me. There wasn't any hope after all. The dark cloud was still following me, and the storm was building.

By age 13, I had endured several major surgeries, years of humiliating medical procedures, seven years with a back brace, and nine months encased in a heavy, hot plaster body cast. And, while the brace left bloodied sores on my hips, ribs, and back at times, it was nothing compared to the emotional scars left by the words of those around me. Good or bad, words have power. Scripture equates this power with life and death (Proverbs 18:21).

Over the years, I had become exceedingly anxious and hypercompliant; but, no matter what I did, it wasn't enough—I wasn't enough. I allowed what others had spoken over me to shape and define who I was. I nurtured and fed a twisted self-image with damaging thought habits that I repeated in my head like a masochistic mantra each night.

Sticks and stones will break my bones, but words they will define me.

It was a practice that eventually generated my own personal storm—a storm that followed me for decades and rose up uninvited and unannounced when triggered by various other tempests of life.

I was filled with an overwhelming sense of impossible shame. How would I cope? How could I live this way? At the time, I didn't understand that I had an emptiness in my soul that only Jesus could fill and, even filled, the journey to wholeness would be long and hard.

Yet, I would spend the next few years trying to fill this void with all sorts of things and people that would only make my loneliness more unbearable, my condemnation more acute, and my guilt more valid. I continued to attract people who used, bullied, abused, and consumed me.

SEX, DRUGS, AND ROCK 'N ROLL

In high school, I became increasingly more insecure and anxious. I was desperate for acceptance and terrified of rejection. Each night, I still practiced my weird habit of making mental notes of everything that was "wrong" with me. I loathed my twisted self-image, and it showed in my life choices.

I studied the "normal girls," who were confident, beautiful, and popular and noted how I was nothing like them. I avoided most of them. But I learned what it took to be "cool," and I became very good at it. I got caught up with the rebels at school—the drug crowd. I learned their language, adopted their "look," and joined them in the smoking area at school.

I discovered how easy it was to attract and manipulate boys, and I enjoyed the temporary illusion of feeling "wanted." I soon learned it didn't take much skill to play the game.

Still, my parents were strict, which, thankfully, limited my freedom and efforts to self-destruct. Most of my friends had absentee parents, so they were almost completely unsupervised. They had parents who were checked out—who let them drink, smoke, and run wild. One friend even got high on the weekends with her mom. My friends had a home life foreign to mine. Even in high school, I still had a 9:30 bedtime.

But my new friends accepted me. Around them, I didn't feel so ugly—I didn't feel like an outcast…mainly because they just didn't *care*. And they didn't know the "real me," which was just how I wanted to keep it. I didn't really know who I was either. And I wasn't the only one whose smile was a façade. This became clear after several suicides swept our school one summer.

I worked hard to hide all my perceived ugliness. I pretended to be tough—I wanted to appear as though I couldn't care less…about anything, when, in reality, I cared *too much* about *everything*. So, I distracted myself with a world of mind-numbing sex, drugs, and rock and roll. I sought a contrived sense of pseudo-love and belonging from destructive relationships, which seemed better than nothing.

My friends were lost in their own depressed world of dysfunctional families and personal problems. Misery loves company. But I never concerned myself with *why* they accepted me; all I knew was that I at least fit in somewhere. So, I enjoyed the short-lived illusion that I belonged, all while remaining "safe" in my protective shell of emotional isolation.

My youngest sister was born when I was fifteen years old, right before Christmas, during one of the darkest periods of my life. I adored her instantly!

That next summer, while grounded, I cared for her while my parents worked. Her sweet smile and unconditional love brought me more joy and hope than I had experienced thus far in life. I had never felt so free to give and receive love.

I treasured the way she snuggled in my arms when I rocked her. Somehow, she felt safe and warm. I showered her with love and affection without fearing rejection. From that point forward, I knew that one day, I wanted to be a mom.

I completed Cosmetology my senior year of high school and, as soon as I graduated, I got a job as a hairdresser and moved into my first apartment. I broke up with my alcoholic boyfriend, who I was tired of mothering, in search of a "real man." My life instantly became all about nightclubs, beach parties, drugs, drinking, and "lookin' for love in all the wrong places."

Because of my chronic self-sabotaging behavior, I was easy prey for unscrupulous men, which resulted in being assaulted and retraumatized repeatedly. I became recklessly promiscuous, wound up in numerous abusive relationships, and eventually developed my own drug and alcohol problem. The times I should have been dead are too numerous to count.

God's mercy was thick in my life. In a vain effort to escape my problems, I moved from Texas to Virginia in the fall of 1987. Of course, that ever-present dark cloud was still following me.

The next year, when I was 22 years old, Jesus revealed Himself to me through the testimony of a precious family I met in Williamsburg, Virginia, and I became a Christian. Though I was spiritually changed, and while my outlook slowly improved, I was still stuck in many toxic patterns. I struggled with insecurity, fear, and a compulsive attachment to destructive men.

SELF-SABOTAGE

At the time I put my faith in Christ, I had been living with an emotionally abusive man for several months. His manic behavior and terrifying outbursts left room for only brief, random illusory surges of love and attention.

Even though his emotional cruelty was sometimes unbearable, and although I was plagued with guilt over the fact that we were "living in sin," I just couldn't bring myself to permanently end the relationship. He always sucked me back in with passionate apologies and promises of the love I so desperately wanted.

My boyfriend suffered his own traumatic childhood, so I tried to be understanding of his conflicted behavior and outbursts. Besides, love didn't seem real unless it hurt. More than anything, I just couldn't bear the thought of being physically alone; so, instead of ending the relationship, I married him.

Our five-and-a-half-year tumultuous marriage was a roller coaster of abuse, rejection, codependency, and adultery, with an occasional day or two of love-bombing to keep me hooked. During that time, I gave birth to my first child. I had never before experienced the euphoric beauty and passion of healthy, human bonding. I was overwhelmed.

Besides Jesus, my daughter became my new reason for *everything*. If it hadn't been for the intense love I had for her, the close counsel and discipleship of my pastor, and the loving support of faithful Christian friends, I might never have had the courage to get out of that toxic marriage. It took me several years of living alone with no outside support while my then-husband lived with his girlfriend out of state before I finally filed for divorce. God knew better than I did what I needed.

The more I have learned about the brain, human bonding, and my own trauma, I believe birth is where it all started for me. During that pre-verbal period, fear and abandonment were wired into my brain. This marked the beginning of years of confusing anxiety, panic attacks, and self-doubt. Many of these issues would wreak havoc in my life before God intervened.

I see now how I created different coping mechanisms—methods I used to protect my mind from the pain of abuse and rejection. By hiding, minimizing, or temporarily "redefining" certain memories, my brain found ways to help me tolerate the intolerable.

Through therapy, I discovered that, all my life, I had been using various methods to cope—to "stay safe" and create order of what sometimes felt like chaos. Survival mode worked for a long time...until it didn't.

Though I had been a Christian since I was twenty-two years old, I still had a thorn in the flesh (2 Corinthians 12:7). Over time, I indeed changed some of the brain habits I had formed years before. As I grew and healed in the Lord, many areas of my thinking improved drastically. However, there were certain memories, and reactions to those memories, that had become more deeply ingrained.

I had unhealthy thought patterns that continued to intensify, harm, and control me. In much the same way a splinter hides under the skin, the truth of the past was always there, ready to trigger blaring warning pains when bumped or pressed, constantly threatening to become infected and cause new harm if not reckoned with.

Time has a way of making the past feel obsolete. We may know we have anxiety, but we are taught or convince ourselves that it's better to simply "get over it and move on." "The past is the past." Or, better yet, take Bob Newhart's advice and "Just stop it!" But denial doesn't turn the lies we tell ourselves into reality; if we pull up those bootstraps too many times, they finally break.

The problem is that even if we stuff it, unresolved trauma affects everything—our choices in life, the treatment we'll tolerate, how we respond to conflict, relationship dynamics, how we do business, how we'll raise our children, and how we give and receive (or refuse) love.

Not that many years ago, I remember lying in a heap on my bathroom floor crying out to God, "What is *wrong* with me? Please, please, please! I can't do this anymore—make these feelings go away. I *need* you, Lord!" Little did I know what the answer to that prayer would look like.

To comfort all who mourn...to give them beauty for ashes, the oil of joy for mourning, the garment of praise for the spirit of heaviness..." (Isaiah 61:2-3)

TRUTH DROP SESSION WEEK 1

Abandonment, Loneliness

Inhale the Truth and Exhale the Lies

Choose one Prayer Oil from the Appendix that you'll use for the prayer step during each Truth Drop Session. Choose five Affirmation Oils to use consistently and in the same order as directed for all nine weeks. Feel free to choose one of the suggested six-oil bundles from the Appendix or select your own.

Remember, you will pray and practice all five steps every morning and every evening for one week before moving on to the next week's Truth Drop Session. You can be as flexible as you like with your journaling.

Many of us have areas of abandonment that we need to deal with from our past. Whether it originated from a mother-infant separation at birth (even if only temporary), childhood neglect, a divorce, a hospital stay, or even a bad experience at summer camp, many of those feelings get trapped in our soul. Allow God to heal these areas in the way only He can. He has promised never to leave you or forsake you.

Breathe deeply, as you reflect, meditate, and embrace the meaning of each Truth Drop, and internalize the reality of who God is and what He says about you.

Anoint your forehead, temples, and brainstem with your Chosen Prayer Oil and pray:

> *Lord, help me to see myself the way You see me—to know and remember that You have orchestrated my steps and given me freedom in Christ. You have loved me in my wretchedness and washed me clean. You have transformed me into something beautiful and valuable. Remind me that regardless of who lets me down, You never will. Regardless of who may forget me, You will never forget.*
>
> *In Jesus' Name, Amen*

1. TRUTH DROPS

Anoint: Apply 1-3 drops of Affirmation Oil #1 on each wrist.

Speak Truth Affirmation: God cares about me; He always has. Even when I thought I cried alone, He was right there with me, experiencing my pain and counting my tears as precious. He stored each one in His bottle of remembrance! God memorized every moment of my suffering. It all mattered.

He soothes and restores my soul. He holds me close. Though He said that one day, sorrow, death, pain, and crying would be banished forever, He comforts me now in my current situation because He cares for me. The God of Heaven knows and loves me. He has compassion for me, and I matter to Him. I am safe. I am loved. I am healing.

Speak Affirmation Support:
- *The Lord is near to the brokenhearted and saves the crushed in spirit.* (Psalm 34:18)
- *You number my wanderings; Put my tears into Your bottle; Are they not in Your book?* (Psalm 56:8)
- *God will wipe away every tear from their eyes; there shall be no more death, nor sorrow, nor crying. There shall be no more pain, for the former things have passed away.* (Revelation 21:4)

2. TRUTH DROPS

Anoint: Apply 1-3 drops of Affirmation Oil #2 on the back of the neck.

Speak Truth Affirmation: God knit me together in my mother's womb. He did not forget me and He did not abandon me. He wept when I wept, so what I went through mattered to Him. Others have failed me, but God did not. He looks on me with compassion and love. My soul is calm and quiet.

My name is engraved on His hand and He thinks of me all the time. He named me before I even knew Him and He is healing me more and more each day. I feel His love and His supernatural comfort. I belong to God. I am cared for. I am not forsaken. I matter.

Speak Affirmation Support:
- *Can a woman forget her nursing child, that she should have no compassion on the son of her womb? Even these may forget, yet I will not forget you. Behold, I have engraved you on the palms of My hands; your walls are continually before Me.* (Isaiah 49:15-16)
- *Surely, I have calmed and quieted my soul, like a weaned child with his mother; like a weaned child is my soul within me.* (Psalm 131:2)
- *When my father and my mother forsake me, then the Lord will take care of me.* (Psalm 27:10)

3. TRUTH DROPS
Anoint: Apply 1-3 drops of Affirmation Oil #3 over the heart.

Speak Truth Affirmation: I am not alone. In His mercy, He saved me. He will not waste any of my suffering. He is healing and transforming what I've been through into a masterpiece that will glorify Him. He is a tender Father to me. I am thankful for my story, and I'm willing to face the pain, so I can release it all to Him. My trials will be an asset, not a liability. I am healing. I am special to Him. I am protected.

Speak Affirmation Support:
- *For you did not receive the spirit of bondage again to fear, but you received the Spirit of adoption by whom we cry out, "Abba, Father."* (Romans 8:16)
- *O Lord, You hear the desire of the afflicted; You will strengthen their heart; You will incline Your ear to do justice to the fatherless and the oppressed...* (Psalm 10:17-18)
- *He will be with you, He will not leave you nor forsake you; do not fear nor be dismayed... He found him in a desert land, and in the howling waste of the wilderness He encircled him, He cared for him, He kept him as the apple of His eye.* (Deuteronomy 31:8, 32:10)

4. TRUTH DROPS
Anoint: Apply 1-3 drops of Affirmation Oil #4 on the edges of each ear.

Speak Truth Affirmation: When I fail, God feels compassion for me and not disgust. He is restoring me. He delights in showing me love and mercy, and He isn't irritated by me or easily angered. God is cheering for me! He doesn't want to punish me or see me harmed. Jesus died for me. He loves me, and He is patient with me. He is for me and not against me. I am at peace in His presence.

Speak Affirmation Support:
- *He chose us in Him before the foundation of the world, that we should be holy and without blame before Him in love, having predestined us to adoption as sons by Jesus Christ to Himself, according to the good pleasure of His will.* (Ephesians 1:4-5)
- *The Lord is near to those who have a broken heart and saves such as have a contrite spirit.* (Psalm 34:18)
- *I cry out to God Most High, to God who fulfills His purpose for me. He will send from heaven and save me; He will put to shame Him who tramples on me. God will send out His steadfast love and His faithfulness!* (Psalm 57:2-3)

5. TRUTH DROPS
Anoint: Apply 1-3 drops of Affirmation Oil #5 on the bottom of each foot.

Speak Truth Affirmation: God thinks good thoughts about me. Because of His great love for me, my Heavenly Father sees me through the lens of Christ's righteousness, rather than my sin. I am precious in His sight, so He never tires of loving me. God has compassion for me in my weakness. He delights in me as His beloved child. I am cherished. I am favored. I am at peace. I have a bright future.

Speak Affirmation Support:
- *How precious also are Your thoughts to me, O God! How great is the sum of them! If I should count them, they would be more in number than the sand; when I awake, I am still with You.* (Psalm 139:17-18)
- *As a father pities his children, so the Lord pities those who fear Him.* (Psalm 103:13)
- *But you, O Lord, are a shield about me, my glory, and the lifter of my head.* (Psalm 3:3)

JOURNAL PROMPT: What memories did God bring to your mind during this session? Write them down.

Ask the Lord to search you and reveal any toxic thoughts, memories, or trauma that He wants you to release to Him. Concentrate on becoming self-aware of your feelings and emotions: Anger? Shame? Sadness? Fear?

What emotions are you feeling? Where are you feeling them? When have you felt them before? Anoint yourself with your Prayer Oil by applying it directly to the place where you feel the emotion and ask the Lord to touch you—to heal you.

Ask God to also show you any bitterness or unforgiveness that you've harbored and forgive and release that, too.

Allow yourself to experience the pain or loss; but, this time, ponder the fact that Jesus was there with you the whole time, tenderly holding your soul and looking upon you with love and compassion, and looking ahead to your bright future.

How does that thought make you feel? Write out your experience and anything else the Lord shows you during this session. Pray and express your gratitude to God for what He is doing in you.

CHAPTER 2
The Fine Art of Denial

I can't think about that right now. If I do, I'll go crazy. I'll think about that tomorrow.—Scarlett O'Hara, *Gone with the Wind*

We all bury certain painful memories to some degree. Sometimes it's emotional procrastination; other times, it's a defense mechanism that kicked in years ago because we weren't ready or able to deal with the event at the time it happened. A safety switch kicked on to protect our mind from being overwhelmed.

But, sometimes, we *never* get around to dealing with it. It's like that cluttered shed out in the back yard full of spiders and boxes of junk. We keep it locked tight and plant flower beds around the shed to make it look pretty. By hiding the mess, we put off the hard work we know needs to happen.

For years, I thought I could "handle it." The anxiety, the triggers, the hyper-vigilance, the striving, the horrible panic attacks…the *shame*. I didn't know exactly how to explain it or even know what it was, but I sure knew how it felt! "It" was controlling me in more ways than I wished to acknowledge or believe. The only thing I had a pretty good handle on was hiding it all.

During therapy, things started to unravel and make sense: My obsessive pursuit of a "safe" environment (especially for my children), my chronic neck and shoulder pain that mysteriously appeared and disappeared repeatedly, and my consistent fear of never "doing it right." I had cried out to God repeatedly to make all these feelings of dread go away—to help me trust Him more—to do "better" somehow. For a long time, it seemed like He didn't hear me. I couldn't even seem to trust God in the right way!

I discovered that I wasn't a "neat freak" after all. Well, I was, but it wasn't part of my "personality" as I had always thought. My obsessive pursuit of a perfectly organized home was more a desperate attempt to create order from the confusion and chaos of my past than anything else. I have often told friends and family that a cluttered house makes my head feel cluttered—I can't "think" in a messy room.

You see, I could control clutter, but I had little control over the toxic thoughts berating and attacking my soul, which were relentless and seemed to have a mind of their own.

MEMORIES BURIED ALIVE DON'T JUST DIE

One recent morning, I had an enlightening experience. I woke up to familiar pain: My neck and shoulder were on fire again (this has been a chronic issue for years). By the second day of the flare up, I oiled up and stayed in bed with my TENS unit, trying to get it under control. As I laid there listening to audio books, I noticed that I was having trouble relaxing any of my back muscles. They just wouldn't release. My whole shoulder area had seized up.

I turned off my audio book, and I began to deliberately contemplate how this pain felt familiar and why. I considered my childhood. I started to realize that this persistent pain reminded me of something from the long-ago past, but I couldn't recall what it was. As far as I could remember, most of the back pain I experienced when I was a child was related to surgery or healing from surgery. But this felt different... yet familiar.

Then I remembered! A memory flooded my mind of the first night I had to sleep with my back brace. I was in first grade. I remembered the horror and shock of how it *felt* when the straps and screws were all tightened. I could feel the burning pain in my shoulders, the suffocating tightness around my hips, and how claustrophobic the metal collar felt wrapped around my neck.

It seemed to swallow me, and the pain was intense. But the worst part was feeling overwhelmed by the thought that this pain wasn't going away—that this horror was my life *from now on*. I felt scared, helpless, and trapped.

I had always remembered the day I first got my brace, but it had always been like watching a movie. This time, I recalled how it all *felt*, emotionally and physically. I felt it like I was there!

That first night, my mom couldn't stand the cries coming from my room, so she asked my dad to go into my room and take the brace off me until morning. The doctors had instructed me to wear it 24 hours a day (except to bathe or swim); so, the next night, even with bloody pressure sores on my hips and back, I was forced to learn to sleep in my brace.

Each time I had to have my brace tightened or replaced (because I had outgrown it), there was pain to face all over again. I did finally get used to my brace, just as the doctors assured me I would; but a different type of pain replaced the physical pain—shame.

The greatest sources of our suffering are the lies we tell ourselves. —Elven Semrad

It has always been such a mystery to me why my lower back just "goes out" without having stressed or injured it in any way. It was the same with my neck and shoulders (though it is a distinctly different kind of pain). Recently, I read how trauma can get "stuck" in the nervous system and the pain may recur throughout one's life in the form of mysterious chronic pain.[12] That made sense to me.

The first time my lower back ever "went out" was after an injury I incurred during my first marriage. After the injury, I was in excruciating pain and unable to move for over a week. This same pain recurs to varying degrees every year or two and usually lasts close to a week. Perhaps the body does indeed remember.[13]

A WANDA WORLD

Although physical pain often contributed to my anxiety, it was the emotional pain that more consistently took center stage. On top of experiencing anxiety, I also felt the stress of trying to hide it.

---

12   *The Body Keeps the Score*, by Bessel van der Kolk M.D., Penguin Publishing Group; Reprint edition (September 8, 2015)
13   *The Body Remembers*, by Babette Rothschild, W. W. Norton & Company; Illustrated edition (October 17, 2000)

One of my greatest fears was that others would see me the way I secretly saw myself. So, I kept on going, kept juggling all the plates…kept trying harder to convince myself that everything was perfectly fine.

Emergency mode felt normal because it was how I had lived for years. I felt like I had to hold it all together and create a haven of beauty, order, and worth for my family. I became very good at it on the outside, but I didn't *feel* it on the inside. Sometimes, the words instinctively came to mind, "If only I had more faith."

In the recent Marvel television series, *Wanda Vision*, the main character uses her superpowers to create a false reality: a vintage sitcom with a world of happy families. In order to cope with her past trauma and avoid the immediate pain and loss in her life, Wanda protects her fake-reality by deceiving even herself. And it works. Until it doesn't.

Eventually, Wanda's fabricated sitcom-world gets "glitchy." She seems confused; and slowly, her false reality starts to crumble. There were parts of me that could relate to Wanda and her collapsing reality.

> "The worst thing I can think of has already happened to me and I can't change it. I can't undo it. I can't control this pain anymore. And I don't think I want to, because it's my truth."—Monica Rambeau, *Wanda Vision*, Episode 7

UNTANGLING THE LIES

It may sound strange, but slowly, it seemed as though my role as a "biblical wife and mother" had become more real and significant than I was as a child of God—as a unique person. Obviously, the whole story would never fit into this chapter; but it was as if the "doing" for my husband and children—homemaking included—had become my identity.

It's complicated, and I'm still working through it, but I kind of wonder if the genuine beauty and nobility of serving one's family, and my intense desire for connectedness, as well as the mysterious bonding that I had missed, caused me to derive *too much* personal value from our family dynamics and, to a certain degree, romanticize it.

"Too much individuality leads a person to disconnect from those around him; too much togetherness and a person begins to feel life is determined by those around him, helplessly dependent on others' emotional vibes.

Our identity—our sense of who we are—fuels everything in our lives. And that identity can only come from God, no matter how noble, pure and right our relationship desires."—Christopher Riordon, boundless.org

For years, I never discussed with others my own past trauma, sin, or abuse—I didn't even allow myself to think about it. I focused on Ephesians 5:12, *"For it is shameful even to speak of the things that they do in secret."* But I was recently surprised to notice that I had somehow neglected the verses that immediately followed:

"But when anything is exposed by the light, it becomes visible, for anything that becomes visible is light. Therefore it says, 'Awake, O sleeper, and arise from the dead, and Christ will shine on you." (Ephesians 5:13-14)

Paul seemed to be saying that what happened to me actually mattered; and that I should allow the light of Christ to shine on it, so that I could fully process my pain in a healthy way.

During the writing of this book, it occurred to me. What if, instead of binding the demons from my past, Jesus wanted to break the chains of trauma that *bound me to them*, so that I could finally truly live?

Then they cried to the Lord in their trouble, and He delivered them from their distress. He brought them out of darkness and the shadow of death and burst their bonds apart. (Psalm 107:13-14)

Instead of desperately trying to keep myself "safe" by avoiding the evil from my past, I realized I could stop giving it power over me. God could use what I went through for a purpose, and maybe someone else could be helped because of it. My pain wouldn't be wasted!

DON'T USE THAT WORD!

No matter what I called it, deep down I knew that so much of what I had gone through had been trauma; but for years it was easier to redefine it, or to just make it "no big deal." If I had kept my mouth shut, if I had tried harder, if I had been a good girl, if I hadn't been so sensitive, if I had been more lovable, if I had done *something* differently, bad things wouldn't have kept happening, and I wouldn't be hurting so much now.

> *You may be ignoring what God is trying to tell you, running from the parts of you that He wants to heal.*—Curt Thompson, MD, *Anatomy of the Soul*

Sometimes we gaslight ourselves because things are so confusing and painful that we choose to deny the reality of the experience entirely. We pretend it didn't happen the way we remembered it, that we "brought it on ourselves," or we engage in some other mental gymnastics to make it all less horrible. But rejecting your reality is dangerous…and it doesn't work, anyway.

I remember wondering if my twisted, misshapen body might be some sort of a consequence of my "mistaken existence." If my birth was a mistake, it seemed to make more sense that my body came with so many "defects."

So, when discussing theology, I felt most comfortable focusing on "the depravity of man." *That* I could relate to! Since the only thing I deserved was Hell, what right did I have to protest *anything*? I deserved whatever I got.

Throughout my life, I experienced abandonment and abuse by numerous people and in different ways—it's complex; but, for years, I couldn't even stand the word "abuse" spoken aloud. It irritated me. To me, it was an overused word that smacked of whining and drama. It was all about someone stuck in the past or trying to get attention. What could be worse than "making a big deal out of nothing?"

Abuse was supposed to be about black eyes, broken bones, and bloody violence. I hadn't suffered any of that. My wounds hadn't left scars that could be seen. Instead, they left shadow scars that whispered in the dark.

So, my self-talk was always about toughening up:
- "Just get over it and stop moaning."
- "Why do you care what anyone thinks?"

- "Just get it right next time and stop doing stupid things."
- "That's what you get."

I convinced myself that I had brought everything upon myself. All the pain, all the rejection, all the shame, all the torment, and all the abuse had happened because I just wasn't *enough*.

Helpless. Guilty. Trapped. Voiceless. Stuck.

If it was my fault, then I could keep trying to make it better, and I would still somehow be in control. If it was someone else's fault...well, what was I supposed to do with *that*? I needed to *make* it my fault, so that I could try to fix it—so that I could change the whole concept of pain.

I have a high tolerance for physical and emotional pain. As a child, I learned to "take it." But I also learned how to hide whatever bad feelings managed to slip through the cracks. Showing pain or weakness made me pitiful and vulnerable—it made me a target for more torment.

There was so much that I had never recognized as trauma until recently—until describing it out loud to my therapist. It was like watching an optical illusion suddenly transform—some sort of hidden, cognitive misconception unraveling before my eyes.

"There is no greater agony than bearing an untold story inside you."
—Maya Angelou, *I Know Why the Caged Bird Sings*

BUCK UP, COWBOY

I had experienced things that were obviously wrong. Had I watched the same abuses happen to anyone else, I easily would have seen it—why had I minimized it all in my own life? This realization rocked my world. I guess to me, it had just been part of reality. Pain was comfortably familiar.

Grace is freeing me to no longer minimize, justify, or deny my losses, but to face them with integrity and grieve over them. Coming out of denial about past losses has been critical to my healing process.—Nancy Groom, *From Bondage to Bonding*

I always wondered why so many people couldn't just forgive and forget and move on like I had. Why couldn't they just put it out of their minds and not make such a big deal out of everything? When women came to me for counsel, I was frequently baffled, and sometimes even resentful. Why couldn't they just get over it and move on like I had had to?

One problem with developing a high pain tolerance is that you eventually expect other people to have one, too. Because I hadn't allowed myself to "feel" and process my own painful emotions—because I had denied and stuffed the reality of my own trauma into hidden parts of my soul, I often wound up minimizing or, worse, dismissing the emotional needs of others.

If we do not transform our pain, we will most likely transmit it.—Richard Rohr

Viewing other people's circumstances through the lens of the pain I was hiding distorted my perspective. I wince when I recall the bad counsel I sometimes gave while in ministry; but it was the counsel I strictly adhered to myself. I was painfully consistent. If what I believed was real, it had to be real for everyone else, too. Things continued to slowly crumble.

I thought I was simply good at "forgiving and forgetting." I believed that seeing myself as an undeserving worm meant that I had simply learned humility. If everyone else could just learn this trick, they'd be okay, too. They'd be more thankful for what they had, like I had learned to be. I didn't know that all those stuffed emotions were toxic or that I failed to see myself the way God saw me. I was arrogantly blinded by my own self-deception.

Though I knew, believed, and taught all the verses that said so, I failed to fully *embrace* the fact that God had created me in His very image—that His own beloved Son viewed me with such love, compassion, and worth that He had died for me, so that I might live!

FOR ME?

I knew it and I believed it, but I hadn't fully internalized it. Even after over 30 years as a Christian, deep down, I still struggled to consistently believe that God's *unconditional* love could truly be for me.

I believed that He forgave me the moment I put my trust in Him, but I struggled with how poorly I demonstrated my thankfulness for His sacrifice—how I constantly failed to "be what He wanted me to be," so I doubted that He would *keep on* forgiving me.

I subconsciously kept waiting for the *boom!* I behaved as though I needed to repay Him for what He had done for me by being sorry *all the time!* As if anyone could ever repay such extravagant heavenly grace!

Of course, I knew that none of us is good enough, that "all have sinned and fall short of the glory of God" (Romans 3:23)" and that it's only because of the death and resurrection of Jesus that any of us are saved. I believed the Gospel long ago when I first put my faith in "Christ alone." My theology was solid, so what was wrong with me?

I *knew* all these things, but there was this nagging feeling I couldn't shake. What if I had gotten some crucial part of some minute doctrine wrong; and what if I were to ultimately discover that, just like always, I had failed to get it right, and I *still* wasn't "good enough?" These were the thoughts that attacked me at my weakest or haunted me in the dead of night—brain habits that were unrelated to what I knew to be true.

Since I hadn't allowed myself to grieve and properly process my past, or to even acknowledge or think about the trauma that had warped my understanding of self and shaped my thinking, I was still being controlled by it all. And it was impacting *everything*. It had also caused me to view God through a distorted lens—a lens that made Him appear detached, harsh, and critical.

Even though I knew and believed the truth of God's Word, I had been trained to see myself through the lens of rejection: unwanted, worthless, ugly, less-than, and perpetually *wrong*. So, too often, I struggled with doubts that God could possibly love me enough to keep forgiving me over and over again—someone who had always been in trouble for everything.

I knew that God was merciful and longsuffering with His people, but at weak moments, I battled the temptation to see God through the lens of my past—to see Him as critical and harsh, eager to punish me the first time I messed up or accidentally "did it all wrong."

So, even now, when these feelings creep back in, if I don't proactively resist the lie with the Truth of God's Word, I am in danger of being tormented again by anxiety and a subtle fear of impending condemnation. Maybe you've had similar struggles. It doesn't have to stay this way.

JOY COMES IN THE MORNING

After years of trying to deal with all of this myself, God led me to a professional Christian therapist who patiently walked me through many distressing memories, pointing out to me the brain habits I had established. She helped me to gain a healthier perspective of the traumatic experiences that I had always minimized, ignored, or hidden. We worked together to untangle the many dysfunctional responses I had developed over the years.

Though I still have a lot of prayer, brain retraining, and hard work ahead, I'm finally learning to acknowledge and embrace the truth of my past as part of my unique story. Instead of pretending it was no big deal, I'm honestly processing it all, as I heal and move forward in hope. This is my desire for you, too.

In combination with therapy, my Truth Drops sessions have helped me to ease the whole process in a gentle, relaxing, and consistent manner. In a way, it feels like, once I was prepared to do the hard work of healing, God started rewriting my story. But, in truth, I know that He had it all planned out for me before the foundation of the world. Now He is simply rewiring my responses. God is *still* writing my story, just as He is writing yours. So, reject the lies, embrace the truth, and watch God transform it all into something healing and powerful!

If you've experienced any sort of grief or trauma, it changes you. It is woven into the fabric of who you are. You can honestly observe the pain for what it is, move past the damage that was done, and learn to sort the truth from the lies. Then you will be better able to release it to the Lord.

He designed your story to include pain, but now He wants to heal you in such a way that He can reframe it as an asset in your life instead of a liability. As my precious friend and suicide-survivor, Crystal, recently pointed out, "God won't erase your trauma, but He can turn it into your *superpower!*" As you heal, God can use you to help inspire and equip others to do the same. He can use it for His glory to draw and heal others.

I don't have it all figured out, but I'm now giving myself permission to feel and process my past. I'm learning to truly release all the hurt to the Lord, so that I can heal, grow, and love deeply and without restraint.

God's healing power can help you to gently grieve the loss of what you believe could or should have been, and then release the destructive thought patterns and memories that have harmed you and held you back. I have found using this approach to rewire my brain extremely productive, gentle, and spiritually healing. I hope you are finding the same freedom and success!

TRUTH DROP SESSION WEEK 2
Stuffed Emotions, Denial

Inhale the Truth and Exhale the Lies

Practice all the steps below every morning
and every evening for one week.

During your prayer time today, God may begin to reveal false
perceptions or stir memories of deep hurts you didn't realize were there.
Rather than pushing the thoughts away, ask God to help you bravely feel
and examine them. Invite Him to heal you and help you to view it all
through new eyes, with Him holding your hand and healing your heart.
You can trust Him.

Breathe deeply, as you reflect, meditate, and embrace the meaning of
each Truth Drop, and internalize the reality of who God is and what He
says about you.

Anoint your forehead, temples, and brainstem with your Chosen Prayer
Oil and pray:

Heavenly Father, help me to trust you completely. Search my heart and know me.
Help me to examine my memories and thought processes and compare them to how
You want me to view them. Reveal to me the secret places You want to heal. Please,
Lord, renew my mind! Give me ears to hear, eyes to see, and a heart to receive.

Thank You, Lord, for helping me to better understand and interpret my
past so that it can no longer control me. Thank You for renewing my
mind and giving me Your strength and Your peace! And thank You for
helping me to remember the thoughts that You think toward me!

In Jesus' Name, Amen

1. TRUTH DROPS

Anoint: Apply 1-3 drops of Affirmation Oil #1 on each wrist.

Speak Truth Affirmation: I can look back on my past, even the painful parts, with hope for the future. I am resting in His love and care because I know He's always there. I am satisfied with Jesus. I am not defined by what anyone has said or done to me in my past. I am not defined by title, rank, grades, or job description. God has plans for me and my future. I am not helpless. My thoughts and ideas matter, and I am fully capable of achieving all my goals. God is for me. I am strong. God has a plan and purpose for me. I am confident and at peace.

Speak Affirmation Support:

- *I will restore to you the years that the swarming locust has eaten…* (Joel 2:25)
- *God is our refuge and strength, a very present help in trouble. Therefore, we will not fear though the earth gives way, though the mountains be moved into the heart of the sea, though its waters roar and foam, though the mountains tremble at its swelling… "Be still, and know that I am God."* (Psalm 46:1-3,10)
- *You will keep him in perfect peace, whose mind is stayed on You, because he trusts in You.* (Isaiah 26:3)

2. TRUTH DROPS

Anoint: Apply 1-3 drops of Affirmation Oil #2 on the back of the neck.

Speak Truth Affirmation: I do not need to question or doubt myself. God searches my heart for me, and reveals to me the truth, as I focus on His Word. He knows me better than I know myself, and He is for me, not against me!

He is using my past to strengthen and grow me and to create in me spiritual endurance. I am confident. I am competent. My future is secure.

Speak Affirmation Support:

- *O Lord, you have searched me and known me! You know when I sit down and when I rise up; you discern my thoughts from afar.* (Psalm 139:1-2)
- *Search me, O God, and know my heart! Try me and know my thoughts!* (Psalm 139:23)

- *We also glory in tribulations, knowing that tribulation produces perseverance; and perseverance, character; and character, hope...* (Romans 5:2-4)

3. TRUTH DROPS

Anoint: Apply 1-3 drops of Affirmation Oil #3 over the heart.

Speak Truth Affirmation: I no longer need to hide who I am. I am dealing with my past, so that I can better live in the present. God sees and knows the real me and He still loves me. I will not allow the thoughts or actions of others, real or perceived, to intimidate or confuse me. I am not defined by my critics or by my outward appearance. I am confident. I am loved. I am appreciated.

Speak Affirmation Support:
- *I will rejoice and be glad in Your steadfast love, because You have seen my affliction; You have known the distress of my soul...* (Psalm 31:7)
- *Let us then with confidence draw near to the throne of grace, that we may receive mercy and find grace to help in time of need.* (Hebrews 4:16)
- *For the Lord sees not as man sees: man looks on the outward appearance, but the Lord looks on the heart.* (1 Samuel 16:7)

4. TRUTH DROPS

Anoint: Apply 1-3 drops of Affirmation Oil #4 to the edges of each ear.

Speak Truth Affirmation: No matter where I go or what I do, God is with me. He saved me and delights in my company. He calms my spirit like a father soothes an infant. Even when He asks me to do hard things, He holds me fast and gives me strength. God celebrates me, as His child. I am safe. I am held. I am revived.

Speak Affirmation Support:
- *The Lord your God is in your midst, a mighty one who will save; He will rejoice over you with gladness; He will quiet you by his love; He will exult over you with loud singing.* (Zephaniah 3:17)
- *Where shall I go from Your Spirit? Or where shall I flee from Your presence? If I ascend to heaven, You are there! If I make my bed in Sheol, You are there! If I take the wings of the morning and dwell in the uttermost parts of the sea, even*

there Your hand shall lead me, and Your right hand shall hold me.
(Psalm 139:7-10)

- *You who have made me see many troubles and calamities will revive me again; from the depths of the earth You will bring me up again...* (Psalm 71:20-21)

5. TRUTH DROPS

Anoint: Apply 1-3 drops of Affirmation Oil #5 on the bottom of each foot.

Speak Truth Affirmation: I put my full trust in the Lord, not in my own ability to protect myself. He is turning my sorrow into joy. I will no longer suffer under the weight of accusations and criticism. He has turned my shame into praise. I am saved. I am no longer an outcast; I am a treasured child of the King of Kings.

The Lord is my protector and my glory. When I am tempted to be downcast and ashamed of the memories, He lifts my gaze toward Heaven. He transforms my dishonor into honor and joy. I will use my story to tell of His marvelous works.

Speak Affirmation Support:

- *My heart rejoices in the Lord...I smile at my enemies, because I rejoice in Your salvation.* (1 Samuel 2:1)
- *The ransomed of the Lord shall return and come to Zion with singing; everlasting joy shall be upon their heads...sorrow and sighing shall flee away.* (Isaiah 35:10)
- *You shall no longer be termed Forsaken, nor shall your land any more be termed Desolate...for the Lord delights in you...* (Isaiah 62:4)

JOURNAL PROMPT: What memories did God bring to your mind during this session? Write them down.

Ask the Lord to search you and reveal any toxic thoughts, memories, or trauma that He wants you to release to Him. Concentrate on becoming aware of your feelings and emotions: Anger? Shame? Sadness? Fear?

What emotions are you feeling? Where are you feeling them? When have you felt them before? Anoint yourself with your Prayer Oil by applying it directly to the place where you feel the emotion and ask the Lord to touch you—to heal you.

Ask God to show you any bitterness or unforgiveness that you've harbored and forgive and release that, too.

Allow yourself to experience the pain or loss; but, this time, ponder the fact that Jesus was there with you the whole time, tenderly holding your soul and looking upon you with love and compassion and looking ahead to your bright future.

How does that thought make you feel? Write out your experience and anything else the Lord shows you during this session. Pray and express your gratitude to God for what He is doing in you.

CHAPTER 3

Human Bonding

Two are better than one... (Ecclesiastes 4:9)

Human bonding is one of the greatest gifts God has given mankind. It's a result of the mysterious biological "glue" that binds two people together—the magnetic link that makes it nearly impossible for two people to forget one another, even if one of them were to try. No matter what happens, there will always be a part of them that won't forget.

In marriage, Scripture describes this as two people becoming "one flesh." During sexual intimacy, the sense of touch is stimulated; hormones and endorphins are released; scents and memories are forged; and taste and sight are recorded in the mind. The limbic system is fully engaged.

As a couple surrenders themselves to one another, all this and more promotes intense bonding and ties two people together emotionally, and perhaps even spiritually (consider Paul's warning in Scripture against fornication in 1 Corinthians 6:16-18).

Research on the brain continues to validate this fact. During sexual arousal and climax men and women release an amazing hormone called oxytocin. There is a reason that scientists call oxytocin the "hormone of love." The release of oxytocin increases trust and affection in a relationship, promotes powerful intimacy, and helps to form emotional attachments.

THE MATERNAL BOND

Another important time of oxytocin release is during childbirth and lactation. It's easy to see how God has designed us to bond in families in order to love, support, and provide for one another. Consider how much we will put up with from our own family that we would never tolerate from strangers.

To truly grasp the importance of bonding and to examine where things can get derailed, we need to go back to the beginning–our beginning— to our first bonding experience (or, perhaps, the lack of one).

In Isaiah, the Bible refers to the compelling compassion (bond) most mothers feel for their own children in order to point out that even if the unthinkable were to occur, and a mother were to forget her child, God's love (bond) would remain steadfast.

Can a woman forget her nursing child, that she should have no compassion on the son of her womb? Even these may forget, yet I will not forget you. (Isaiah 49:15)

As an unborn infant grows and develops (Psalm 139:13), he is, in many ways, protected and nurtured within the secret walls of his mother's womb. This is the first time a child "bonds" to another human being. Even in the womb, the senses are engaged. The baby can hear the mother's heartbeat, as well as her voice and body systems. He can taste, feel, and even see.

Based on the way a newborn instinctively knows, responds to, and prefers his mother above all others, makes one wonder if the pre-born may have even more senses that perhaps are lost at birth—senses that we haven't yet discovered.

God's intricate creation of an infant in the womb, and even childbirth itself, are awesome mysteries (Psalm 139:14). The fascinating bond between a mother and child is what makes it possible for a brand-new mother to gladly die, if need be, for the human being who, only moments before, she had never set eyes upon. In utero, we share not only our mother's DNA, but we share her nutrients, hormones, chemistry, and sometimes even her emotions, as well. If there is a twin or multiples, that bonding may also include siblings.

The bonding relationship intensifies during breastfeeding through all five senses: scent, taste, touch, sound, and sight. Calming hormones, endorphins, and other chemicals are released. Eye contact is made, soothing verbal cues are expressed, and breast milk offers taste and warm, satisfying nourishment and contentment that comes from the process of suckling. Mutual scents are shared and memorized by the brain.

HEAR MY CRY

As a mother comforts her child's cries, soothes him, lovingly responds to his needs, and proves to be a steady, nurturing figure, a child learns to trust—to bond in a healthy way to the one who, at least in the beginning, is his whole world.

This is one of the reasons I feel so strongly about answering the cries of a newborn, rather than leaving him/her to "cry it out" alone for long periods of time, as certain controversial parenting books encourage. Our babies need to know they aren't alone in this big, scary world.

An infant doesn't understand why one moment they are warm and can smell, hear, and even taste mommy's skin, and then the next moment they are cold and alone in a dark room. They may even wonder if this alone feeling will last forever!

> *If two lie together, they keep warm, but how can one keep warm alone?* (Ecclesiastes 4:11)

Could it be that a pre-verbal infant, perhaps predisposed to trauma through a biological labyrinth of DNA, is forever impacted from being separated from his/her mother? For those who have experienced this broken bond, maybe it's the thing that makes trusting people so difficult.

Throughout our lifetimes, we attach ourselves to others in numerous ways and to varying degrees. But the most significant bonding is typically experienced in parent-child and husband-wife relationships.

THE BROKEN BOND

Sometimes these relationships are tragically interrupted, damaged, or destroyed. Bonds are broken through abandonment, trauma, betrayal, abuse, neglect, or even death. For a developing child, regardless of the degree, trauma can cause lasting damage and drastic changes to the actual structure of the brain. Journalist Gabrielle Glaser said it well in her book, *American Baby: A Mother, A Child, and the Shadow History of Adoption:*

> "Many doctors and psychologists now understand that bonding doesn't begin at birth, but is a continuum of physiological, psychological, and spiritual events which begin in utero and continue throughout the postnatal bonding period. When this natural evolution is interrupted by a postnatal separation from the biological mother, the resultant experience of abandonment and loss is indelibly imprinted upon the unconscious minds of these children."

Whether caused by maternal separation or marital collapse, a severed bond results in changes in the brain chemically, hormonally, and developmentally as our bodies try to cope with the distress of unexpected or premature separation. This disruption or "rewiring" can have drastic effects on our ability to trust, relate to, and interact with others—especially those closest to us. In other words, it can injure or cripple our ability to create healthy, intimate relationships with others, even with those who truly love and care for us. One distressed adoptive mom described the disruption this way:

> "Attachment happens in the womb; the children hear voices and experience environment while they are being nurtured within their mother. Once the twins were born, they were taken from this familiar setting and placed in a new home with new voices and new smells. Only to be taken three months later to yet another home, with completely different voices, smells, and sights.
>
> This is traumatic to a young developing child. Their brains go into survival mode, and they learn not to trust or be nurtured. This is the reality. Don't minimize the effects this can have on children. It changes who they are."—Anonymous Adoptive Mom

There is a growing awareness regarding the significance of bonding and attachment during child development. There are support groups, books, and seminars designed to help adoptive parents and others to cope with the unique struggles their children face.

However, what I couldn't find were any practical tools for the average non-psychotic adult who struggles with the common, everyday emotional and/or spiritual results of abandonment, real or perceived. Of course, professional counseling is sometimes crucial, but I also wanted a practical tool to use at home.

As I searched for information, I began to realize there may be reasons for some of the anxieties and sometimes irrational fears I struggled with as an adult adoptee. I noticed a pattern, as certain anxieties had similar triggers (and resulting responses). Could it be there were bonding issues in my heart God wanted me to work through?

The Lord is near to the brokenhearted and saves the crushed in spirit. (Psalm 34:18)

Bonding or attachment issues can also be present in those who weren't adopted. Children who suffered a long or traumatic separation from a parent or caregiver at a young age, who had an emotionally absent or abusive parent, or a child whose twin died at birth may also have bonding, abandonment, or attachment issues.

A betrayed, abused, or abandoned spouse may struggle with bonding issues, as well. Rejection digs its claws in deep. Security, love, and mutual happiness are replaced with self-doubt, shame, and grief. Everything is colored by the underlying, painful reminder of what could have been, but isn't.

> "Betrayal, addiction, and trauma weave a design of continually recycled wounds that create an overarching pattern of compulsive relationships."—Patrick J. Carnes

BOND WITH JESUS

As I've contemplated this type of loss in my own life, I believe that when processing trauma, we should recognize and learn to "feel" the pain of what we lost—the thing that we never properly took the time to face and grieve.

Maybe circumstances forced us to be brave for the sake of others. Perhaps we were too young to even understand it at all, or it may be that we deliberately set it aside because it just hurt too much. God calls us to take our pain to Him.

For the Lord has called you like a wife deserted and grieved in spirit, like a wife of youth when she is cast off, says your God. (Isaiah 54:6)

As we bond with Jesus, our healing is inevitable. Even the mere act of touching the hem of His garment healed the woman with the 12-year issue of blood (Matthew 9:20-22). When we stop expecting people to heal our deepest hurts, and turn to intimately bond with our Savior, change is certain.

Like sanctification, healing from the hurts of emotional trauma may be a life-long process of personal insight and growth, but there is joy in the journey and, by bonding to your Father in Heaven through His Son, Jesus Christ, there really is abundant joy and hope, not only for the future, but for the here and now.

My prayer is that you will discover why you may sometimes react in ways that are confusing and learn practical, achievable ways to deliberately change your responses. I want you to feel confident in your own skin, become more successful, and enjoy closer, healthier relationships. While this may be an emotional journey, I hope you also find it a spiritual one!

May the God of hope fill you with all joy and peace in believing, so that by the power of the Holy Spirit you may abound in hope. (Romans 15:13)

TRUTH DROP SESSION WEEK 3

Betrayal, Rejection

Inhale the Truth and Exhale the Lies

Practice all the steps below every morning
and every evening for one week.

Rejection and/or betrayal may have originated during your childhood, but they can be experienced any time in our lives within different types of relationships. The most intense hurt seems to come when we feel we were rejected or betrayed by a parent or spouse, but it can also happen during friendships, sibling bonds, or work or school relationships.

If we don't invite God to heal the secret places of our heart, the trace negative emotions left behind can quietly impact all our future relationships. If we don't deal with them, we risk spending our lives with a hidden protection shield that will keep us from healthy bonding. We will struggle with freely giving and receiving the level of love that God intended. Invite God to heal your heart and embrace the One who is always faithful.

Breathe deeply, as you reflect, meditate, and embrace the meaning of each Truth Drop, and internalize the reality of who God is and what He says about you.

Anoint your forehead, temples, and brainstem with your Chosen Prayer Oil and pray:

Heavenly Father, help me to sense your presence and know that I am Yours. Surround me with the knowledge of Your love. Help me to learn from You, rather than from the destructive lessons of trauma and betrayal. I have often viewed myself through the eyes of the demons from my past, but I choose to believe You above all others.

Help me to remember that when people put me down, I am still valuable to You. A rejection or betrayal is not a reflection of my worth. My identity is in You. Help me to remember that I am precious to the King of Heaven. And help me to truly forgive and release the rejection and betrayal of the past, so that I might love as You love. Help me to replace those toxic thoughts with Your beautiful Truth (Psalm 118:5-6)!

In Jesus' Name, Amen.

1. TRUTH DROPS

Anoint: Apply 1-3 drops of Affirmation Oil #1 on each wrist.

Speak Truth Affirmation: God has not discarded me. He created me for meaningful things because He loves me. Though I have not always seen my own value, God has always treasured me. Though others have betrayed me, God has always been faithful.

He is a perfect Husband and Father. He will never abandon me. He is my protector, so I boldly stand in His strength! He is all I need. He never minimizes me or leaves me behind. My life is meaningful. I am protected. I am strong. I am loved.

Speak Affirmation Support:
- *For the Lord has called you like a wife deserted and grieved in spirit...* (Isaiah 54:6)
- *Father of the fatherless and protector of widows is God in his holy habitation.* (Psalm 68:5)
- *Your Maker is your husband, the Lord of hosts is His name...* (Isaiah 54:5)

2. TRUTH DROPS

Anoint: Apply 1-3 drops of Affirmation Oil #2 to the back of the neck.

Speak Truth Affirmation: I have a voice, and when I cry out to God, He hears me every single time. He is my advocate and defender. God is on my side, so I don't have to be afraid of anyone. Jesus wins! Because of Him, I am strong, I am bold, and I have the power to make good choices. I am loved, and I am healing. I am safe. My decisions are trustworthy. My future is secure.

Speak Affirmation Support:
- *Out of my distress I called on the Lord; the Lord answered me and set me free. The Lord is on my side; I will not fear. What can man do to me?* (Psalm 118:5-6)
- *I have said these things to you, that in me you may have peace. In the world you will have tribulation. But take heart; I have overcome the world.* (John 16:33)
- *You will no longer suffer reproach. Behold, at that time I will deal with all your oppressors. And I will save the lame and gather the outcast, and I will change their shame into praise and renown in all the earth.* (Zephaniah 3:18-19)

3. TRUTH DROPS
Anoint: Apply 1-3 drops of Affirmation Oil #3 over the heart.

Speak Truth Affirmation: Though people may leave me, God never will. He is steadfast and trustworthy. He is healing the broken places of my heart. I am bonded to Him. He nourishes my soul and holds me close. He is always with me. He comforts me. I am strong. I am courageous. I am overjoyed.

Speak Affirmation Support:
- *He heals the brokenhearted and binds up their wounds.* (Psalm 147:3)
- *Keep me as the apple of Your eye; hide me in the shadow of Your wings, from the wicked who do me violence, my deadly enemies who surround me.* (Psalm 17:8)
- *How precious is your steadfast love, O God! The children of mankind take refuge in the shadow of your wings.* (Psalm 36:7)

4. TRUTH DROPS
Anoint: Apply 1-3 drops of Affirmation Oil #4 the edges of each ear.

Speak Truth Affirmation: Jesus knows my grief. He also suffered loss, betrayal, pain, infidelity, and disloyalty. Because of that, I know He understands my aching heart and, just as His pain had purpose, so does mine. God is for me. He is turning it into an asset in my life. He is working everything out according to His ultimate plan—for my good and His glory.

Speak Affirmation Support:
- *Jesus wept.* (John 11:35)
- *We know that in all things God works for the good of those who love him, who have been called according to his purpose... If God is for us, who can be against us?* (Romans 8:28, 31)
- *The Lord God helps me, therefore I have not been disgraced; therefore I have set my face like a flint, and I know that I shall not be put to shame. He who vindicates me is near...Behold, the Lord God helps me.* (Isaiah 50:7-9)

5. TRUTH DROPS

Anoint: Apply 1-3 drops of Affirmation Oil #5 on the bottom of each foot.

Speak Truth Affirmation: I am not alone. My God is with me! Jesus said He would be with me even to the end of the world! Wherever I go, I do so in strength and courage, because God is there, protecting me, providing for me, empowering me. I am now free to love others, to bless others, to comfort others because I know the love, blessing, and comfort of God. I've been set free, and I can now be who I really am.

Speak Affirmation Support:
- *And behold, I am with you always, to the end of the age.* (Matthew 28:20)
- *Be strong and courageous. Do not fear or be in dread of them, for it is the Lord your God who goes with you. He will not leave you or forsake you.* (Deuteronomy 31:6)
- *Blessed be the God and Father of our Lord Jesus Christ, the Father of mercies and God of all comfort, who comforts us in all our affliction, so that we may be able to comfort those who are in any affliction, with the comfort with which we ourselves are comforted by God.* (2 Corinthians 1:3-4)

JOURNAL PROMPT: What memories did God bring to your mind during this session? Write them down.

Ask the Lord to search you and reveal any toxic thoughts, memories, or trauma that He wants you to release to Him. Concentrate on becoming self-aware of your feelings and emotions: Anger? Shame? Sadness? Fear?

What emotions are you feeling? Where are you feeling them? When have you felt them before? Anoint yourself with your Prayer Oil by applying it directly to the place where you feel the emotion and ask the Lord to touch you—to heal you.

Ask God to also show you any bitterness or unforgiveness that you've harbored and forgive and release that, too.

Allow yourself to experience the pain or loss but, this time, ponder the fact that Jesus was there with you the whole time, tenderly holding your soul and looking upon you with love and compassion, and looking ahead to your bright future.

How does that thought make you feel? Write out your experience and anything else the Lord shows you during this session. Pray and express your gratitude to God for what He is doing in you.

CHAPTER 4

A Trail of Fears

From bitter experience she knew that pictures thrown on the screen of her imagination could seem much more unnerving and terrible than the actual facts.—Much-Afraid, *Hinds Feet on High Places*

Everyone deals with fear at times. Fear in and of itself isn't always a bad thing. In fact, in its proper context, it can be a great gift—a healthy, God-given response to true and present danger. An animal who never feared would likely end up as another creature's dinner. But there's an insidious type of fear—one that's deceitful, destructive, and can even become chronic. This type of fear is crippling and is an enemy to perfect love (1 John 4:18).

I spent most of my life in bondage to a mere shadow of fear, even as a Christian. Fear in its many forms is an insidious and often faceless foe. It stalks you in the dead of night, taunts you with your own imagination, and mocks you with jolting triggers—phantom shadows of the past.

But fear is a liar. And its deception over us is an impotent illusion of power. Trauma has physical and neurological aftereffects; but fear is a weapon of the Enemy powered only by our own willingness to submit to it. Perfect love casts out fear. Jesus, the very essence of love, came to set the captives free. That's a real thing.

Out of my distress I called on the Lord; the Lord answered me and set me free. The Lord is on my side; I will not fear. What can man do to me? (Psalm 118:5-6)

A SHADOW OF FEAR

You've probably heard the term "afraid of your own shadow." Can you recall ever feeling that type of fear—that paralyzing, irrational type of fear that makes you see or hear things that aren't real (you hope!)? Sometimes, as a kid in my bed at night, if I closed my eyes, I imagined the eyes of the beautiful antebellum doll I had received for Christmas glowing red and watching me from her perch on top of the bookshelves on my dresser.

I just knew she was waiting for me to fall asleep, so she could climb down from my dresser and *get me*. Although the fear was all in my head, it caused my body to react as though I was in real physical danger. My heart raced, I perspired, and my breathing rate increased. My mind began to play tricks on me. I could almost hear her climbing down from that dresser!

Thankfully, when I couldn't stand it anymore, and I quickly opened my eyes to check, she was still sitting politely in her regular spot. But I could never bring myself to look at her eyes...just in case! I'm pretty sure that my doll phobia (which haunted me into my 20s) came from a movie I watched with my grandmother when I was too young to process the frightening absurdity of the storyline.

Granted, the old black and white thrillers I watched would probably stir little more than a yawn from today's kids, but they terrified me—so much so, that I couldn't wait until the next time one came on TV, so I could repeat the experience. Why did I go back for more?

There are plenty of good reasons that scary movies are called "thrillers." It's like riding a roller coaster. The slow, teasing ascent up the tracks prepares us for the petrifying ecstasy of false terror! That crashing thrill—that rush of euphoric fear induces a biochemical "high"—a surge of exhilarating adrenaline.

This can be fun and exciting when it's a game—when we're the ones in control of how, when, and under what circumstances we get that occasional rush. But trauma is different; it catches us off guard. It broadsides us when we're weak and vulnerable.

With trauma we're *not* in control. We have no say over what's happening and, often, we have no knowledge of what's going to happen next. Fear of the unknown is an ominous void that we must learn to fill only with faith (Hebrews 11:1).

FRAZZLED

The habit of fear breeds more fear. I've dealt with anxiety and panic attacks all my life. For years, I was acutely aware of and embarrassed by it, so I worked hard to hide it…even from myself. I wanted to be in control of my own life, and that included my emotions. Of course, most of the time, I didn't even know what was happening.

Anxiety was my inner normal. I was often frustrated with myself for losing it over some small thing, even though most of the losing it was only in my head. I was a pro at hiding my reactions, so people rarely knew anything was wrong with me or how I suffered inside. In fact, very few people knew I struggled at all.

I knew my anxiety was becoming increasingly problematic, but I still thought I could handle it. I didn't notice anything significantly wrong unless I was triggered by some random thing, but these triggers had become more frequent and more intense.

I had mini-panic attacks that threw my whole day off and sometimes got in the way of everyday life. To avoid a panic attack, I found myself avoiding certain situations, people, and activities in which I really wanted to participate. I frequently felt anxious and on edge, and I began to recognize it as a growing problem.

One winter, I stopped driving for over a year, and I had to deliberately force myself to get behind the wheel again. My daughters joked about "Driving Miss Stacy" and told me they were concerned I would lose my ability to drive altogether. I laughed, but I secretly shared their fear.

SWITCHING GEARS

I started therapy primarily because I was writing a book on essential oils and human bonding, and I had hit a brick wall. With my research and reflection, I finally realized that, if I was going to have anything legitimate to share with others, there were things from my past that I needed to deal with first. So, with a little encouragement from my friend, Crystal, I searched for a Christian therapist.

This was a big step for me, since I had operated for years under the impression that psychology and Christianity were diametrically opposed, which is why I frequently beat myself up for my emotional responses and struggles. I viewed it as a lack of faith or spiritual discipline.

Little did I know what an eye-opener (and total game-changer) therapy would be! While God rocked my whole world, I put my bonding book on the back burner. While untangling how I had gotten where I was, I started journaling my personal thoughts. Soon, this book began to take shape.

TRAUMA RESPONSES

Everyone responds to danger or trauma differently, so try to examine which type of response to which you're most prone. If you feel threatened by a bad guy in a dark alley, are you the type to fight, run, play dead, or talk your way out of the danger?

The mental health community recognizes four categories for the ways most people react when protecting themselves from harm. All of us subconsciously use different responses depending upon the situation and our relationship to the perceived danger: Fight, Flight, Freeze, and/or Fawn.

Each type of response has healthy and unhealthy ways of showing up in our lives. The goal is to train ourselves to automatically react with the healthy side of our naturally inclined response(s).

- **Fight –**
  - Unhealthy: *Fights back. Defensive. Hurts others before they can be hurt. Needs constant affirmation. Controlling. Entitled. A bully.*
  - Healthy: *Establishes healthy boundaries. Assertive. Courageous.*

- **Flight –**
  - Unhealthy: *Avoids. Hide., Runs away. Becomes reclusive. Secretive. Puts up walls. Obsessive thinking. Perfectionism. Panic and fear. Workaholic. Obsessive cleaning. Hypervigilant. Fearful.*
  - Healthy: *Disengages from unhealthy conflict or arguments. Walks away from toxic relationships. Accurately assesses danger. Sets healthy boundaries.*

- **Freeze –**
  - Unhealthy: *Shuts down. Zones out. Disassociates. Escapes inside head. Brain fog. Difficulty making decisions. Fear of failure. Stuck. Procrastinates. Chronically exhausted.*
  - Healthy: *Self-aware. Stays present/in the moment. Reflective. Deep thinker.*

- **Fawn –**
  - Unhealthy: *People pleaser. Appeases. Dishonestly defends or rescues harmful people. Peace at all costs. Tries to negotiate their way out of danger. Insecure. Codependent. Passive aggressive. Obsessive inner critic. Clingy.*
  - Healthy: *Compassionate. Merciful. Attentive. Fair.*

It's important to remember that the trauma responses described above are not abnormal behaviors. They are *normal* responses to *abnormal* danger. If you suffered through a traumatic experience, the trauma response you experienced was activated by the brilliant brain God gave you to protect you from danger. You are not defective!

Acknowledge the unique intricacies of your own complex mind and be thankful that God wired it into your system to protect you. If you are now in a safe environment, this response is no longer necessary; so, it may be time to do an emotional reset.

COPING MECHANISMS

Too often, we memorize lies that were inadvertently created during or after a traumatic episode by perpetuating them with unhealthy brain habits of repetition. Instead of deliberately rerouting our thoughts to the healing safety of God's Word, our minds find ways to manage those bad feelings ourselves by developing various (and sometimes complex) coping mechanisms.

These methods serve us well by protecting us from being overwhelmed during a vulnerable time. But when they are no longer necessary, they may be holding us back, harming our relationships, or even hindering our overall success in life.

In addition, some of us may have turned to drugs, alcohol, promiscuity, self-harm, food, toxic relationships, porn, or even idolatry in a futile attempt to distract ourselves from the pain of the past. All these distractions are destructive and keep us from any sort of productive solution.

Because of the physiological consequences of trauma, we may continue to experience the same feelings and release the same chemicals that were triggered during a time when we were in real danger. The trick is to learn to tell the difference, so that we can *feel* safe when we *are* safe.

It's interesting how our minds have so much power over what happens in our reality. If we think people are going to dislike us, we kind of make it happen. If we're afraid of bullies, we attract them. If we believe we're weak, *everyone* looks like a giant. It can even affect how others see us.

YOU ARE STRONGER THAN YOU THINK

Notice in Numbers 13 what happened when the Israelite spies went out to scout the situation regarding their enemies. They saw mere men, but they *perceived* them as undefeatable foes, forgetting that God was on their side.: "We are not able…for they are stronger than we are…" (Numbers 13:31)

In fact, the Bible says they saw themselves "as grasshoppers" in comparison! Not only did they see themselves as weak, but they imagined that their enemies also saw them this way: "We seemed to ourselves like grasshoppers, and so we seemed to them." (Numbers 13:33)

If we want to be successful in business, in relationships—in life in general—and want others to view us as competent, we must first see ourselves the way God intended—with inestimable value and great potential.

My biggest fears almost always involved the safety of my kids. I raised ten children without owning a single Lego until my youngest son was well-past the choking-hazard stage (ironically, the same kid swallowed a Lego when he was 15).

I was always thinking ahead. My son-in-law, Daniel, still jokes about the time he was courting our daughter, Christa. Wanting to impress her and surprise her younger siblings, he brought over a bundle of balloons. Terrified of "choking hazards," I swiftly popped each one and threw them away. I had read a news article about the tragic death of a child who had choked on the remnants of a popped balloon and that was all it took—no more balloons in the house.

During my most anxious seasons of life, I entertained in my mind all sorts of dramatic scenarios of danger. In an endless attempt to avoid disaster, I played the "what if" game. I thought I could outwit danger by anticipating all the worst-case scenarios imaginable. Is it any wonder why, when my children were young, I never missed an episode of the television show, *Rescue 911*?

If we aren't aware of what's happening, and if we don't learn to deliberately take captive our thoughts, distress becomes automatic. It can become a mental habit or, again, an addiction! Reverting to anxious thoughts and heightened emotions can become a natural reaction to any sort of stress.

> *"Believe me, when you get to the place which you dread you will find that they are as different as possible from what you have imagined…I must warn you that I see your enemies lurking among the trees ahead, and if you ever let Craven Fear begin painting a picture on the screen of your imagination, you will walk with fear and trembling and agony, where no fear is."*—Hannah Hurnard, *Hinds' Feet on High Places*

This drastically affects our physical health, as well as our overall productivity and success in life. This is what I discovered I needed to change, and I believe you can, too! As you learn to take captive and train your thoughts, your brain changes and heals on a cellular level.

With God's help, we can learn to think new thoughts—we can, by deliberately creating new "brain habits," retrain and literally "change our minds."

Remember, whether you have simply allowed negative thought patterns to hinder your success or you discover you've been operating under unhealthy coping mechanisms, there is hope! Because of the life-changing power of God's Word and the transforming reality of neuroplasticity, you can take control of your thoughts and retrain your own mind.

> *Eventually, as we manage our thinking, the entire state of the brain and our cellular structure shifts and establishes a new and healthy level of balance in the mind, brain and body!* —Carolyn Leaf, *Switch on Your Brain*

TRUTH DROP SESSION WEEK 4
Fear, Anxiety

Inhale the Truth and Exhale the Lies

Practice all the steps below every morning
and every evening for one week.

Perfect love casts out fear, so use this time to embrace God's
overwhelming love for you. We cannot simultaneously embrace both
fear and faith; so, I invite you to trust in and bond with the One who has
the power to transform all your anxieties, so that you can more fully and
completely give and receive love! He changes *everything*.

Breathe deeply, as you reflect, meditate, and embrace the meaning of
each Truth Drop, and internalize the reality of who God is and what He
says about you.

Anoint your forehead, temples, and brainstem with your Chosen Prayer
Oil and pray:

> *Lord, when I am tempted to fear the unknown, help me to have the faith I
> need to trust you completely. Keep me from turning first to other people or
> substances. You are my rock and strength. Remind me to use your Word,
> prayer, and your gift of my five senses to stay present and to think clearly.*
>
> *In Jesus' Name, Amen*

1. TRUTH DROPS

Anoint: Apply 1-3 drops of Affirmation Oil #1 on each wrist.

Speak Truth Affirmation: I have no room for anxiety in my life. Fear
lied to me. God doesn't want to punish me—His grace is perfect. God is
not harsh, unreasonable, or critical. He is kind, patient, loving, and just.
I am redeemed; I am secure in the eternal embrace of Jesus, my Savior.

Because of His loving sacrifice on the cross, I am forever safe. He is compassionate, merciful, and tender. He watches over me. He is all-powerful and, even when I'm weak, He gives me strength. God does not lie; therefore, I know that whatever He says about me is 100% true. I am loved. I am bold and strong. I am capable. God is on my side.

Speak Affirmation Support:
- *I am with you and will watch over you wherever you go…* (Genesis 28:15)
- *My grace is sufficient for you, for my power is made perfect in weakness. Therefore, I will boast all the more gladly of my weaknesses, so that the power of Christ may rest upon me. For the sake of Christ, then, I am content with weaknesses, insults, hardships, persecutions, and calamities. For when I am weak, then I am strong.* (2 Corinthians 12:9-10)
- *You shall not be afraid of the terror by night, nor of the arrow that flies by day…* (Psalm 91:5, ESV)

2. TRUTH DROPS
Anoint: Apply 1-3 drops of Affirmation Oil #2 on the back of the neck.

Speak Truth Affirmation: The Lord is with me, comforting me. He will even be there in death! He won't allow my enemies to have the final triumph—and that includes human and spiritual enemies, as well as the enemies of illness or injury. He has equipped me for the battle! I don't have to be afraid because He is in control of my every breath—each beat of my heart—each cell in my body! He is restoring my soul! I am forever safe. I am at peace. I am protected for all of eternity.

Speak Affirmation Support:
- *Yea, though I walk through the valley of the shadow of death, I will fear no evil; for You are with me; Your rod and Your staff, they comfort me. You prepare a table before me in the presence of my enemies; You anoint my head with oil; my cup runs over.* (Psalm 23:4-5)
- *The Lord is my light and my salvation; whom shall I fear? The Lord is the stronghold of my life; of whom shall I be afraid?* (Psalm 27:1)
- *Are not two sparrows sold for a copper coin? And not one of them falls to the ground apart from your Father's will. But the very hairs of your head are all numbered. Do not fear, therefore; you are of more value than many sparrows.* (Matthew 10:29-31)

3. TRUTH DROPS

Anoint: Apply 1-3 drops of Affirmation Oil #3 over the heart.

Speak Truth Affirmation: I am not afraid of any sort of evil, wickedness, or unknown enemy because He who is within me is greater than He who is in the world. My God is the victor and Satan is a defeated foe! I know who I am in Christ, and I have no need to fear anything because even when I am weak, Jesus in me is strong! In the authority of the mighty name of Jesus, all evil must flee!

Speak Affirmation Support:
- *He disarmed the [demonic] rulers and authorities and put them to open shame, by triumphing over them in it.* (Colossians 2:15)
- *God is our refuge and strength, a very present help in trouble. Therefore, we will not fear though the earth gives way, though the mountains be moved into the heart of the sea, though its waters roar and foam, though the mountains tremble at its swelling... "Be still, and know that I am God."* (Psalm 46:1-3,10)
- *Little children, you are from God and have overcome them, for He who is in you is greater than he who is in the world.* (1 John 4:4)

4. TRUTH DROPS

Anoint: Apply 1-3 drops of Affirmation Oil #4 the edges of each ear.

Speak Truth Affirmation: God knows all about my numerous anxieties, and He brings me perfect comfort! He supplies my every need and brings me joy. I am loved by the Creator of the Universe, and He has equipped me with His strength and the power to overcome my anxieties! My healthy thoughts are clear and unwavering.

I am free to give and receive love from God and from others. The Lord is always with me; even when I don't sense His presence, He is there. He constantly helps and supports me. I am steady. He cares about me, and I delight in Him. I am content. I am at peace. I am confident.

Speak Affirmation Support:
- *In the multitude of my anxieties within me, Your comforts delight my soul.* (Psalm 94:19)

- *And my God will supply every need of yours according to His riches in glory in Christ Jesus.* (Philippians 4:19)
- *Casting all your anxieties on Him, because He cares for you.* (1 Peter 5:7)

5. TRUTH DROPS

Anoint: Apply 1-3 drops of Affirmation Oil #5 on the bottom of each foot.

Speak Truth Affirmation: God has appointed me to bear fruit for Him. He has entrusted me with valuable dreams, goals, and ideas. My dreams, in accord with His Word, are purposeful and powerful. Each day, He strengthens my mind, my body, and my spirit to accomplish His will. I surrender to His plan. I am chosen. I am called! I am productive. I am blessed and blessing others. I am filled with purpose!

Speak Affirmation Support:
- *You did not choose Me, but I chose you and appointed you that you should go and bear fruit and that your fruit should abide, so that whatever you ask the Father in My name, He may give it to you.* (John 15:16)
- *Do not repay evil for evil or reviling for reviling, but on the contrary, bless, for to this you were called, that you may obtain a blessing.* (1 Peter 3:9)
- *And we know that for those who love God all things work together for good, for those who are called according to His purpose.* (Romans 8:28)

JOURNAL PROMPT: What memories did God bring to your mind during this session? Write them down.

Ask the Lord to search you and reveal any toxic thoughts, memories, or trauma that He wants you to release to Him. Concentrate on becoming self-aware of your feelings and emotions: Anger? Shame? Sadness? Fear?

What emotions are you feeling? Where are you feeling them? When have you felt them before? Anoint yourself with your Prayer Oil by applying it directly to the place where you feel the emotion and ask the Lord to touch you—to heal you.

Ask God to also show you any bitterness or unforgiveness that you've harbored and forgive and release that, too.

Allow yourself to experience the pain or loss; but, this time, ponder the fact that Jesus was there with you the whole time, tenderly holding your soul and looking upon you with love and compassion, and looking ahead to your bright future.

How does that thought make you feel? Write out your experience and anything else the Lord shows you during this session. Pray and express your gratitude to God for what He is doing in you.

CHAPTER 5

Lions and Tigers and Triggers, Oh My!

There is no living thing that is not afraid when it faces danger.
The true courage is in facing danger when you are afraid…
—The Wonderful Wizard of Oz

Grief, personal trials, and everyday conflicts happen to everyone. If we are emotionally healthy and strong, we are likely better equipped to deal with those situations without lingering negative results. The resulting pain doesn't stick. It's felt, processed, healed, and released. We're able to move on, hopefully with valuable memories or lessons learned.

But depending on the conditions, trauma can leave indelible, sometimes crippling, marks on the soul. Trauma could involve an assault, a violation, an injury, a chronic illness, abuse, war, bullying, or a combination of any or all these things.

Trauma happens when we experience something that overwhelms our emotional ability to handle it at the time. If we are already at a disadvantage because of a physical, emotional, or situational weakness, or because of pre-existing trauma, we are more likely to experience lasting debilitating results.

THE BRAIN PROTECTS THE BODY

When the trauma first happens, our body alerts us to danger, and the fight or flight hormone, adrenaline, is released into the bloodstream, which is a *great gift* if a bear is chasing us or if we need extra strength or speed in order to save ourselves (or someone else) during an emergency. It's a tool God hardwired into our bodies to equip us to deal with physical danger. In an emergency, it's meant to save our life.

But we weren't designed to live in emergency mode forever. The stress hormone, cortisol, is also released to balance things out and get us back to normal, but it can have lingering consequences when released habitually. So, if these biochemical reactions get out of whack or become chronic, it stresses and fatigues the body, wreaks havoc on our overall health, and can change the brain physically. We can literally become addicted to fear.

> *I have set before you life and death, blessing and curse.*
> *Therefore, choose life…* (Deuteronomy 30:19)

NEUROPATHWAYS

Think of the earth as your brain and running water as the stress hormone, cortisol. In science class, you probably remember learning about erosion. Over time, the release of water over the surface of the earth and rock causes erosion, which creates all sorts of new and deep pathways (picture the Grand Canyon). If cortisol consistently floods the surface of the brain over long periods of time, the brain has literally, *physically changed*.

Trauma leaves a literal trail of fear behind. Which means that later, when some familiar experience "triggers" a memory, the brain reverts to those automatic pathways, and fear instantly becomes an overwhelming flood of emotion. Although we may now be safe, the brain once again goes into emergency mode in ways that may seem irrational and confusing to onlookers (and maybe even to us), especially if we can't consciously remember the incident or details that created the original response.

> *Trauma results in a fundamental reorganization of the way mind and brain manage perceptions. It changes not only how we think and what we think about, but also our very capacity to think…For real change to take place, the body needs to learn that the danger has passed and to live in the reality of the present…—The Body Keeps the Score*, by Bessel van DER Kolk, M.D.

THE TRIGGERS OF EVERYDAY LIFE

As we discussed, in distress, our brain memorizes passageways from stimulus to response at nearly unperceivable speeds. A trigger causes our body to respond without asking our mind permission. Likewise, we can also automatically recollect a *positive* memory when any of our five senses are stimulated by something familiar.

Note how in the following two examples, triggers can be either good or bad:

- *A Good Trigger: When Lindsay smells apple pie and turkey roasting in the oven together, the aroma instantly transports her back to a time when she was a child in her grandmother's kitchen at Thanksgiving. Everyone was happy, there was plenty of laughter, and her grandparents made her feel loved and special.* This is an example of the "good feeling" from a memory being spontaneously triggered by scent.

- *A Bad Trigger: When Kristy watches a movie or news program with a scene of someone being assaulted or attacked, she feels overwhelmed by the same physical sensations and emotions she experienced during a traumatic event from her childhood—a time when she felt helpless and terrified. Her heart rate and breathing speed up, she perspires, and she feels agitated and nervous.* This is an example of the "bad feeling" from a past trauma spontaneously triggered by sight and sound.

Each person responds differently to trauma, but some common triggers will make more sense once you start to examine them. For instance, after John was molested by his alcoholic uncle when he was eight years old, he internalized the experience. His uncle threatened him that if he ever told anyone, it would crush his mother and people would know that it was "all John's fault."

And, because John's body had seemingly betrayed him by sexually responding to the assault, he felt confused and humiliated. He internalized these feelings and subconsciously owned the guilt of his abuser and hid the shame he felt. Can you imagine what some of John's triggers are now—triggers that may cause those feelings of helplessness and shame to suddenly appear?

- Smelling alcohol on someone's breath
- Being put in a position of weakness by a large or powerful man

- Being blamed for someone else's actions
- Feeling vulnerable or helpless in a situation

Whether or not a person has experienced trauma, a trigger can bring to mind even simple negative experiences from the past: The death of a grandmother, a bad break up, a church split, hurtful words, a negative experience at work or school—the list goes on.

Bad things happen to people all the time. But when the triggers become chronic, cause frequent panic attacks or anxiety, or the reaction becomes overwhelming, it's probably past time to deal with it. If you have baggage, don't wait. Get help.

I'LL THINK ABOUT THAT LATER

Sometimes, we experience a distressing event that we can't acknowledge or deal with properly at the time either because we are too young or because we are unable or unequipped to process it. So, our brain helps to protect us by finding ways to put off the painful experience until a time when it won't overwhelm us.

Within the panic cycle, it is not the body that responds incorrectly. The body responds perfectly to an exaggerated message from the mind. It is not the body that needs fixing, it is our thoughts, or images, or negative interpretation of our experiences that we must correct in order to gain control of panic.—Dr. R. Reid Wilson[14]

The problem is that we're just stuffing emotions we eventually need to face. For our own protection, our brain may temporarily ignore or hide the emotion from our conscious mind. We may bury the entire memory deep in our subconscious.

This is a God-given process, so these coping mechanisms are a temporary mercy. Still, God didn't intend for this to be a permanent solution. The pain remains waiting under the surface. So, when something happens to remind our brain that the trauma is still there, it triggers an involuntary physical/emotional response that may bring back all the same feelings, sensations, and physical reactions we felt in our past.

---

14   R. Reid Wilson, Ph.D., *Breaking the Panic Cycle*, Phobic Society of America, 1990, p. 18,19

We're reminded that the "splinter" is still there, waiting to be addressed. Even though it may be many years later, and we may be perfectly safe now, our brain loops back to the trauma buried deep within us.

As long as the trauma is not resolved, the stress hormones that the body secretes to protect itself keep circulating, and the defensive movements and emotional responses keep getting replayed.—Bessel Van Der Kolk, *The Body Keeps the Score*

Some responses can be more severe than others. For me, responses to those triggers have ranged anywhere from simple avoidance behavior to full-blown panic attacks complete with heart palpitations, trembling, and hyperventilating—I *feel* the original trauma in my whole mind and body.

PANIC ATTACKS

This experience is even worse if, for some reason, I'm unable to immediately access an environment where I feel safe. Feeling trapped, falsely accused, or ganged up on triggers some of the most distressing responses for me.

Once, in my early 20s, a panic attack landed me in the emergency room. Convinced I was either having a heart attack or a stroke, my boss called 911. I felt like I couldn't breathe, my heart raced uncontrollably, my chest felt tight and heavy, my hands shook violently, my legs were weak, and my arms felt like they were going numb.

In that instance, I don't know what triggered my panic attack. Maybe it was a result of where I was emotionally at the time. I was a single parent in the middle of a divorce and a lot of financial stress. Maybe the circumstances were stirring up old feelings of abandonment or helplessness. I don't know. I'm not sure there is always a recognizable trigger to panic attacks. I've even had panic attacks in the middle of the night. Our minds are so complex!

As we've learned, there are times when one or more of our five senses (sight, sound, touch, taste, or *smell*) activate these auto-responses. This is one of the reasons I believe so strongly that leveraging essential oils is a healthy (and powerful) brain retraining tool.

Instead of going to those negative, destructive thoughts, we deliberately create new auto-responses that spontaneously redirect our triggered memory to God's Word. Instead of battling the lies with methods of self-protection, we use the Sword of the Spirit (Ephesians 6:17). In our weakness, He proves Himself strong (2 Corinthians 12:9). We need to learn to turn to Him, rather than trying to control it all ourselves.

You are making headway! Keep it up! Internalize that truth, repeatedly. Always remember that what you diligently practice is what you will master. Inhale the truth – exhale the lies. You are in training!

And which of you by being anxious can add a single
hour to his span of life? (Luke 12:25)

TRUTH DROP SESSION WEEK 5

Triggers

Inhale the Truth and Exhale the Lies

Practice all the steps below every morning
and every evening for one week.

If you've lived with "splinters" of hidden hurts hiding under the surface, invite Jehovah Jireh, the Great Physician, to do His work in your mind and soul. Pursue the One who gives the "peace that passes all understanding."

Breathe deeply, as you reflect, meditate, and embrace the meaning of each Truth Drop, and internalize the reality of who God is and what He says about you.

Anoint your forehead, temples, and brainstem with your Chosen Prayer Oil and pray:

Heavenly Father, I know that if a child of mine were to ask for a loaf of bread, I wouldn't give him a stone. And You are a much better parent than I am—You are perfect. So, I ask you now, Lord, to heal me from destructive and dysfunctional thought patterns. I believe and trust that You will help me.

You are my Great Physician. I pray that you would heal my mind, make sense of my memories, heal my emotions, my hormones, and my spirit. Thank you for your gift of oils, Lord; and, as I use them, and combine them with your Holy Word, I pray you would renew my mind, and do a great work in me, Lord. Thank you.

In Jesus' Name, Amen

1. TRUTH DROPS

Anoint: Apply 1-3 drops of Affirmation Oil #1 on each wrist.

Speak Truth Affirmation: I am free because of Jesus. I have given my burdens over to the Lord, and I thank him for taking care of them in His way. I release all my worries because I'm free from the burden of the past. It's not my job to figure it all out. I am confident and at peace because Jesus is guarding my heart and mind. I am safely armed with the Sword of the Spirit. I am protected by my Heavenly Father. I am safe.

Speak Affirmation Support:
- *Do not be anxious about anything, but in everything by prayer and supplication with thanksgiving let your requests be made known to God. And the peace of God, which surpasses all understanding, will guard your hearts and your minds in Christ Jesus.* (Philippians 4:6-7)
- *Take the helmet of salvation, and the sword of the Spirit, which is the Word of God.* (Ephesians 6:17)
- *Keep your heart with all vigilance, for from it flow the springs of life.* (Proverbs 4:23)

2. TRUTH DROPS
Anoint: Apply 1-3 drops of Affirmation Oil #2 to the back of the neck.

Speak Truth Affirmation: I am safe because Jesus loves and protects me. Jesus hears me, and He is healing me. He has rescued me from my fears because I trust Him. The Lord who made heaven and earth is helping me. His Holy Spirit is keeping me on track by helping me build new pathways in my brain, so that my mind is healing and renewing each day! I am growing and getting stronger every day!

Speak Affirmation Support:
- *I will both lie down in peace, and sleep; for You alone, O Lord, make me dwell in safety.* (Psalm 4:8)
- *I sought the Lord, and He heard me, and delivered me from all my fears.* (Psalm 34:4)
- *When I am afraid, I put my trust in You.* (Psalm 56:3)

3. TRUTH DROPS

Anoint: Apply 1-3 drops of Affirmation Oil #3 over the heart.

Speak Truth Affirmation: Because Jesus is with me, I won't be afraid—He is my God. He loves me and is making me strong. I will love deeply, as I am loved, which leaves no room for fear or isolation. I am at peace. I am strong. I am connected. I am free to love and be loved.

Speak Affirmation Support:
- *Greatly loved, fear not, peace be with you; be strong and of good courage.* (Daniel 10:19)
- *Let all who take refuge in You rejoice; let them ever sing for joy, and spread Your protection over them, that those who love Your name may exult in You.* (Psalm 5:11)
- *You will not fear the terror of the night, nor the arrow that flies by day, nor the pestilence that stalks in darkness, nor the destruction that wastes at noonday.* (Psalm 91:5-6)

4. TRUTH DROPS

Anoint: Apply 1-3 drops of Affirmation Oil #4 to the edges of each ear.

Speak Truth Affirmation: When I feel anxious or fearful, I know it is a symptom and not part of my identity. God is healing me. I have been empowered by the God of the Universe with the Holy Spirit to rule my feelings, so that I can experience and share His love more freely with others.

I will not be controlled by fear. I was created to walk in the Spirit, not in the flesh. When I am weak, He who is within me is strong. I will use my past as an asset, and not see it as a liability.

Speak Affirmation Support:
- *You have turned for me my mourning into dancing; You have put off my sackcloth and clothed me with gladness...* (Psalm 30:11)
- *I lift up my eyes to the hills. From where does my help come? My help comes from the Lord, who made heaven and earth.* (Psalm 121:1-2)
- *Then they cried to the Lord in their trouble, and He delivered them from their distress.* (Psalm 107:13)

5. TRUTH DROPS

Anoint: Apply 1-3 drops of Affirmation Oil #5 on the bottom of each foot.

Speak Truth Affirmation: I trust God and not my old perceptions. I am thankful for the protection of my temporary coping mechanisms, but I release them now with gratitude. I am free from the danger of the past. God is my shield and my protection, and He is leading and guiding my steps.

Speak Affirmation Support:
- *Trust in the Lord with all your heart and lean not on your own understanding; in all your ways acknowledge Him, and He shall direct your paths.* (Proverbs 3:5-6)
- *He will cover you with his pinions, and under His wings you will find refuge; His faithfulness is a shield and buckler.* (Psalm 91:4)
- *Fear not, for I am with you; be not dismayed, for I am your God. I will strengthen you, yes, I will help you, I will uphold you with My righteous right hand.* (Isaiah 41:10)

JOURNAL PROMPT: What memories did God bring to your mind during this session? Write them down.

Ask the Lord to search you and reveal any toxic thoughts, memories, or trauma that He wants you to release to Him. Concentrate on becoming self-aware of your feelings and emotions: Anger? Shame? Sadness? Fear?

What emotions are you feeling? Where are you feeling them? When have you felt them before? Anoint yourself with your Prayer Oil by applying it directly to the place where you feel the emotion and ask the Lord to touch you—to heal you.

Ask God to also show you any bitterness or unforgiveness that you've harbored and forgive and release that, too.

Allow yourself to experience the pain or loss; but, this time, ponder the fact that Jesus was there with you the whole time, tenderly holding your soul and looking upon you with love and compassion, and looking ahead to your bright future.

How does that thought make you feel? Write out your experience and anything else the Lord shows you during this session. Pray and express your gratitude to God for what He is doing in you.

CHAPTER 6

Just Who Do You Think You Are?

What if this critical person is in your own head? What if you are the person with the problem? What if you have met the enemy, and he is you?—Henry Cloud and John Townsend, *Boundaries*

The whispering shadows of shame and condemnation lurked in the corners of my mind. Too often, I agreed with their accusations. It just made sense. The best thing for me to do was to simply accept them and keep repenting every second of every single day. Forever. I would never have admitted it to myself or anyone else, but that was often how I approached God. Constant ambiguous, fretful repentance consumed much of my prayers.

I eventually realized that the obsessive inner focus on my depravity was way too similar to my childhood list of self-deprecatory "faults." I had created a habit of focusing on all the wrong things. There was almost no room for pondering value, gratitude, tenderness, or love. In a strange compulsive arrogance, I mistook self-criticism and contempt for godly humility. Self-loathing won't save us any more than good works will.

Condoning or minimizing our own abusive or unjust treatment, or even abusing ourselves, will not make us godlier. In fact, I'm learning that this sort of gnostic thinking has less to do with humility and more to do with pride and dysfunction. It certainly doesn't please or bring glory to God.

THE VOICE OF THE INNER CRITIC

"Don't even try; you're going to make a fool of yourself."
"Everyone knows what a loser you are."
"You're just going to blow this again."
"Nobody wants you around."
"People are going to laugh at you."

Everyone's inner critic has a different voice, but we all have one. The toxic words repeating in your head like a broken record were likely recorded there long ago by people from your past. When they were first spoken over you, you may have been unable to understand properly or deal with your emotions, but the words stuck.

For some reason, we always remember or absorb the negative things. Five people might compliment us at work, but if that one person in the office criticizes us, *that* is the conversation we will most likely dwell on and remember.

Hurtful words often are absorbed too easily and memorized by the soul. That's why Scripture teaches the importance of guarding the tongue and likens it to an untamable fire and "a restless evil, full of deadly poison" (James 3:8). Words can hurt…and they *stick*. So sometimes it takes the body time (and deliberate effort) to retrain, rewire, and heal from the words we absorbed so long ago.

The Enemy knows all our weaknesses and he will try to use them to keep us in bondage (Ephesians 6:12). I recall years ago hearing devastating words from a man who claimed to love me: "You're a deformed piece of sh**!" I was twenty-three years old, and I already secretly agreed with those words before they were spoken.

The Enemy will use our past hurts to find our underbelly every time. Don't absorb the lies! They are much easier to weed out before you allow them to take root! But if you have already absorbed lies about yourself, there is hope! Hateful words are only illusions, and the truth shatters illusions.

These toxic thoughts tend to point out all the ways we're not good enough—all the ways we secretly fall short. They also remind us to worry about what other people might think about us, what they're probably saying about us behind our back, and the numerous ways everyone else is *better* than we are.

And, when we're trying to get up the nerve to do something amazing—something creative, exciting, or bold—that "helpful" voice tries to stop us by suggesting all the stupid ways we may blow it, and how people will probably laugh at us, and maybe we'll be viewed as foolish or ridiculous. Maybe we will fail, and everyone will see what a nothing we are.

It may remind us of the pain of the last time we trusted people and got burned, or the time we tried to be brave and landed on our face in front of the whole world. Yeah. That critical voice is our voice of safety, right? It's just keeping us out of trouble. No, unfortunately, that voice of "safety" serves up its own helping of trouble.

> *The gap left in the child's soul...centers on the shame of his perception that his real self, his inner person, is unacceptable, not enough, is inadequate.*—Nancy Groom, *From Bondage to Bonding*

If you've been listening to your inner critic, that's another type of brain habit; and it's a damaging one! When you want to move forward in some way...either with your business, an important relationship, school, or some other productive direction in your life, it stands in the way of your progress or success. But it's difficult because, like a deceptive friend, your inner critic is a familiar voice—one you've trusted for years.

RISE UP!

Admit it, sometimes, even when you want to be brave, you vacillate because you wonder if the critical words lingering in your mind might be true. You're paralyzed and confused because you know what the right thing to do is, but that voice keeps holding you back from rising up and actually *doing* it.

In Isaiah 54:4, we're assured with the words, "Be not confounded, for you will not be disgraced..." This is the same verse that goes on to remind us that "you will forget the shame of your youth." Isn't that interesting, especially as we consider the way so much of our baggage is associated with things that happened to us in our childhood—times when we were young and vulnerable in some way?

In the verse, the word "confounded" communicates worry and confusion, traits of a fearful and troubled mind. The very opposite of the "sound mind" Paul says we have access to in 2 Timothy 1:7.

Earlier, in 1 Corinthians 14:33, Paul tells us that "God is not the author of confusion, *but of peace...*" and he brings it home a second time when he instructs those who are married to an unresponsive spouse not to chase him or her, but instead, to let them go. "In such cases the brother or sister is not enslaved. *God has called you to peace.*" (1 Corinthians 7:15, emphasis mine) God knows the value of a sound and peaceful mind.

> *He who loses sight of the Word of God, falls into despair;*
> *the voice of heaven no longer sustains him; he follows only the*
> *disorderly tendency of his heart.*—Martin Luther

That critical voice keeping your mind in turmoil and confusion isn't coming from God. In fact, it likely came from trauma—things done to you, said to you, or that happened to you. You may have memorized that voice or its aftereffects during times when you felt pain, fear, shame, abandonment, or rejection. Sometimes pain is what we know.

Because of a dysfunctional past, stress now feels comfortable and almost normal, but it's an illusion. Regardless of how mild the hurt, the Enemy of your soul enjoys whispering to you the worst memories of your distress. And the more you listen, the stronger his power over your mind, and the stronger the brain habits become.

In fact, the Enemy will try to maximize even the mildest trauma by amplifying its aftereffect to torment you. Then he uses the fear of it happening again to train you to avoid loving and living in peace and freedom, as God created you to do.

Fear comes from the Enemy—the Father of Lies; it does not come from God. But perfect love casts out fear (1 John 4:18). Again, God assures us that He has given us *a spirit of power, and of love, and of a sound mind (2 Timothy 1:7)*. We just need to tap into it. We must become deliberate with our thoughts!

The Reprograming:
"When God calls you to something, He will strengthen you to do it!"
"There are plenty of people who have confidence in you!"
"This time, you're going to make it!"
"You are worthy of love and respect!"
"People are going to love your ideas!"

IMAGO DEI [15]

In 1 Kings 19:12, we learn that God, regardless of the turmoil going on around us, speaks to us in a "still, small voice" [a delicate whisper]. He also says His sheep know His voice when He calls them by name, and He knows them (John 10:27).

So, let's stop listening to impotent voices that we know aren't His, and commit to getting still, listening to, and *knowing* the quiet voice of Power and Truth. Respond to the lies with the power and authority of Truth—God's Living Word.

Years ago, after mustering up all the nerve I had, I made a meek and carefully worded request of someone I loved. But this person looked me in the eyes and scoffed, "Who in the Hell do you think you are?" At that moment, my spirit sank. I was crushed, and I remember the sting of realizing not who I *was*, but who I was *not*. And I walked in that forsaken identity for many years.

However, I now know that it's not as much *who* I am, as it is *Whose* I am. I am a daughter of the King of Kings. I am made in God's image—created for good works. I am bought with a price. I am fearfully and wonderfully made. I was lost, and now I'm found, because Jesus came looking for me! I am His (Isaiah 43:1)! *That* is what makes my heart sing and gives me hope. I will listen to His voice alone.

Do you know who you are? When we listen to the lies in our head that tell us we're worthless, the Enemy tempts us to believe they're true. We can't forget our secret sins or all the ways we've been rejected or

---

15   Image of God

minimized by those in our past. But God addresses this head-on in Isaiah 54:4 when he tells us that our shame is forgotten. He promises, *"You will forget the shame of your youth…"*

> *You shall no longer be termed Forsaken…for the*
> *Lord delights in you…. (Isaiah 62:4)*

STAND FIRM

Learning to be assertive after living life with a warped perception of self and personal value can be confusing—at times, it may even feel uncomfortable or selfish. But showing ourselves compassion and valuing what God values is healthy and right. I'm not suggesting you should push someone else under the bus; I'm saying you shouldn't throw *yourself* under it!

Although we should try to avoid conflict when possible (Romans 12:18), "avoiding conflict at all costs" is a mark of codependency, and it is not healthy, nice, or godly.

Even as a strong, assertive Christian, there will likely be legitimate times when He calls us to suffer for Christ's sake. During those times, surrendering to a higher ultimate purpose teaches us sacrifice and true humility. We can trust God that none of it will be wasted or fruitless. But it's important to understand that unnecessarily submitting to a tyrant doesn't make us holier.

In Acts 16, Paul and his men were attacked by a crowd of bullies. Their tormenters tore their clothes, beat them with rods, and bound them and threw them into prison. But Paul was a Roman citizen and he called them on it. The entire incident was illegal, so somebody's job was on the line:

> *But when it was day, the magistrates sent the police, saying, "Let those men*
> *go." And the jailer reported these words to Paul, saying, "The magistrates*
> *have sent to let you go. Therefore come out now and go in peace." But Paul*
> *said to them, "They have beaten us publicly, uncondemned, men who are*
> *Roman citizens, and have thrown us into prison; and do they now throw*
> *us out secretly? No! Let them come themselves and take us out."*

The police reported these words to the magistrates, and they were afraid when they heard that they were Roman citizens. So they came and apologized to them... (Acts 16:22-40)

Neither Jesus nor His Disciples cowered under abusive men. They never falsely confessed to sin for the sake of peace or better treatment. And when they suffered, they did so willingly, sacrificially, and with purpose. They made their decision with strength and a confident understanding of their personal worth. The Disciples walked boldly in their identity in Christ (and, in Paul's case, his right as a Roman citizen). And God used it.

PEOPLE PLEASING

I spent years feeling manipulated and often used by people around me. I sometimes promoted and empowered the very people who viewed me as less-than. I attempted to please the unpleasable, yet no one was ever pleased, least of all me.

Giving in to manipulation never satisfied anyone or resulted in any sort of true peace or resolution. In fact, it almost always blew up in my face. Submitting to or complying with a bully may temporarily put off conflict, but it won't end well. In the end, it may even result in additional trouble. If you are in that situation (at school, work, church, home, or wherever) get help immediately.

In conflict, I often felt obligated to be the "bigger person" and apologize, whether or not I had actually done anything wrong. This sort of psychological dishonesty is emotionally maddening, spiritually damaging and, in the end, further empowers abusive or dysfunctional people.

After becoming a Christian, I rightly owned my own sin. I was keenly aware of my own selfishness, reckless behavior, and numerous daily failures. But I also developed a habit of sometimes taking responsibility for the sins of others. "If I hadn't failed in this way, they wouldn't have done what they did."

Personal worth is a critical factor in how we view and respond to everything and everyone around us. When we have a damaged view of self, it affects all our choices: our confidence, our relationships, how we treat people, what we'll tolerate from others, our ability to make good decisions—basically, our overall success in life and in love. In fact, our ability to love others fully and freely is all wrapped up in how well we're able to receive it.

WHO DO YOU SAY GOD IS?

To fully understand our personal worth, we need to have a healthy view of who God is. If we think of God as cruel, or if we view Him as a Creator who looks down from Heaven waiting to zap us every time we do something wrong, then we will think of him as impossible, critical and harsh, and it will be difficult to embrace the knowledge of how precious we are to Him.

To have a healthy relationship with God, it's crucial to understand who He really is. In Matthew 15:16, Jesus asked Peter, "Who do you say that I am?" Peter answered with certainty, "You are the Christ, the Son of the living God."

Jesus knew how important it was for Peter to know and believe He was the Messiah—that the Son had been sent by the Father to save us. He wanted to make sure Peter understood that He and the Father were one (John 10:30), proving God's desire to save the world (John 3:16).

We too must know the true character of our Heavenly Father. If we say we "trust Jesus," but we think of our Heavenly Father as aloof and far away, how can we really trust Him? If we believe God created us, threw us to earth, and left us to fend for ourselves, or if we view Him as distant and uncaring (basically, a negligent parent) how can we really know our Heavenly Father at all? Can we trust a parent who would leave his little child to wander the dangerous world alone?

How does that concept of a father make you feel? Does the perception of God as a detached, hands-off parent make you feel very loved or safe? To me, it feels like abandonment and neglect. And we know that our Father in Heaven is the *perfect* Father, so there's no way we're on our own—it's a slanderous lie we should reject.

He will be with you, He will not leave you nor forsake you; do not fear nor be dismayed… He found him in a desert land, and in the howling waste of the wilderness He encircled him, He cared for him, He kept him as the apple of His eye. (Deuteronomy 31:8, 32:10)

A NEW CREATION

Maybe you've believed the Truth for years, but you find your responses and behavior inconsistent with what you know to be true. Maybe you resort to simply doing "what you've always done." Sometimes we can know something in our head, but our actions don't keep up.

That's why we're learning to renew our mind—so that our mind can work *for* instead of *against* us to retrain our physical brain to match what we truly believe. Then we are better equipped to be doers and not just hearers of the Word (James 1:22).

Don't close your healed eyes to what God has changed. Stop walking in the torment and fears of the past. That's not the abundant life God has for you. Stop hiding in the strange, miserable comfort of familiar pain. Those are old pathways we need to reroute.

If any man be in Christ, he is a new creature: old things are passed away; behold, all things are become new. (2 Corinthians 5:17)

Who do *you* think you are? Do you realize God's own beloved Son laid down His life so that you might live? And it wasn't just to keep you out of Hell. Jesus came that you might have life and have it more abundantly (John 10:10). *Abundant* life! Your personal worth (intrinsic worth) has nothing to do with what you do or how well you perform (extrinsic worth).

Keep in mind, you cannot brain-train your way into a relationship with God. Faith is foundational. Physical exercise (which includes brain-training) is an excellent help in creating spiritually/emotionally healthy habits, "but godliness is profitable for all things, having promise of the life that now is and of that which is to come" (1 Timothy 4:1-11). Be careful not to get it out of order!

VAIN STRIVING

Then I considered all that my hands had done and the toil I had expended in doing it, and behold, all was vanity and a striving after wind, and there was nothing to be gained under the sun… (Ecclesiastes 2:11)

Do not allow your work (or anything else) to compete with Jesus for your heart; that's how idols are formed. If you seek your identity in your work, title, rank, homeschool, ministry, gender, or even your efforts as a loving spouse or parent, you will never be satisfied. You will find your true identity, purpose, and worth only in Him. Have you given Him His rightful place in your life?

He satisfies the longing soul, and the hungry soul he fills with good things… (Psalm 107:9)

If our work becomes the center of our life instead of Jesus, we will likely end up striving instead of thriving. We may find ourselves struggling with exhaustion and persistent anxiety because "we could always do more…or do it better." There will *always* be work to do! So, in the middle of the night when we're trying to sleep, guess what thoughts our mind will be drawn to… "There is so much to do!"

Do not be anxious about anything, but in everything by prayer and supplication with thanksgiving let your requests be made known to God. (Philippians 4:6)

Speak life over yourself! Be assured that your worth is tied to the fact that you are made in God's image and in your position as *His child,* not in what you do or what anyone says about you. As Christians, we serve and obey God out of love for Him; not so that we can *win* Him. There is nothing we could ever do or say to *earn* something as precious as God's love. Jesus did it all! So, who do you say that He is? And *whose* do you say that you are?

TRUTH DROP SESSION WEEK 6

Identity, Self-Image, Belonging

Inhale the Truth and Exhale the Lies

Practice all the steps below every morning
and every evening for one week.

Sticks and stones and broken bones are nothing compared to hurtful words. Too often, those words get filed away in our brain to taunt us even years later, which is why it's so important to reject the lies of the world by knowing the one true God and thinking of His thoughts toward us. We can trust Him with our most tender and delicate memories. Invite Him to heal the raw spots, knowing He loves and cherishes you.

Breathe deeply, as you reflect, meditate, and embrace the meaning of each Truth Drop, and internalize the reality of who God is and what He says about you.

Anoint your forehead, temples, and brainstem with your Chosen Prayer Oil and pray:

Heavenly Father, I come before you in the name of Jesus and ask that you would be with me right now. Allow Your Word to come alive for me. Help me to know you're speaking directly to me. Show me how I can more easily hear and know your loving voice and teach me to reject the critical voice of the Accuser.

Please send your Holy Spirit to walk with me through this journey. Thank you for shaking loose so many memories and revealing areas of bondage in my life. I choose to release them to you now and lay them at the foot of the cross. Thank you, Lord.

In Jesus' Name, Amen

1. TRUTH DROPS

Anoint: Apply 1-3 drops of Affirmation Oil #1 on each wrist.

Speak Truth Affirmation: I am his masterpiece! God created me to glorify Him by walking confidently and unashamed of what He made. Because of what the Lord has done in me, I am beautiful and capable of making a difference in the world. When the Lord looks at me, He is tender, loving, and compassionate. I am of greater value to Him than diamonds or rubies. I matter.

I am a daughter/son of the King of Kings. I am made in God's image—created for good works. I am bought with a price. I am fearfully and wonderfully made. I was lost, and now I'm found because Jesus came looking for me! I am His! I have hope!

Speak Affirmation Support:
- *You shall also be a crown of glory in the hand of the Lord, and a royal diadem in the hand of your God.* (Isaiah 62:3)
- *For we are His workmanship, created in Christ Jesus for good works, which God prepared beforehand, that we should walk in them.* (Ephesians 2:10)
- *I praise You, for I am fearfully and wonderfully made. Wonderful are Your works; my soul knows it very well.* (Psalm 139:14)

2. TRUTH DROPS

Anoint: Apply 1-3 drops of Affirmation Oil #2 to the back of the neck.

Speak Truth Affirmation: I am clothed with compassion, kindness, humility, gentleness, and patience. My past does not define me! I am a new Creation in Christ…chosen, holy, and dearly loved. I am standing firm in the love of Jesus, and I am not to be manipulated, bullied, or intimidated by evil!

Speak Affirmation Support:
- *Therefore, as God's chosen people, holy and dearly loved, clothe yourselves with compassion, kindness, humility, gentleness and patience.* (Colossians 3:12)
- *Therefore, if anyone is in Christ, he is a new creation.* (2 Corinthians 5:17)
- *You shall be far from oppression, for you shall not fear; and from terror, for it shall not come near you.* (Isaiah 54:14)

3. TRUTH DROPS

Anoint: Apply 1-3 drops of Affirmation Oil #3 over the heart.

Speak Truth Affirmation: I am not forsaken, forgotten, rejected, or discarded. I am valuable. I am loved. I am precious in His sight. I was bought with a price—an inestimable price—my Savior's blood was shed on my behalf!

I am a son/daughter of the King of Kings and I choose to believe God, rather than the lies in my head. I am who God says I am. He comforts me and makes me beautiful.

Speak Affirmation Support:
- *You are precious in My eyes, and honored, and I love you...* (Isaiah 43:4)
- *I have named you, though you have not known Me...* (Isaiah 45:2, NKJV)
- *As the bridegroom rejoices over the bride, so shall your God rejoice over you.* (Isaiah 62:5)

4. TRUTH DROPS

Anoint: Apply 1-3 drops of Affirmation Oil #4 the edges of each ear.

Speak Truth Affirmation: I belong to Jesus. I am His. I am not afraid, because I am precious to Him and He loves me. He sees well beyond what I can see. He knows the way. I trust Him because I am His and He loves me. I am God's own precious child. He redeemed me. I am at peace. I am filled with courage.

Speak Affirmation Support:
- *Fear not, for I have redeemed you; I have called you by name, you are Mine...* (Isaiah 43:1)
- *See what kind of love the Father has given to us, that we should be called children of God; and so we are.* (John 3:1)
- *Peace I leave with you; My peace I give to you. Not as the world gives do I give to you. Let not your hearts be troubled, neither let them be afraid.* (John 14:27)

5. TRUTH DROPS

Anoint: Apply 1-3 drops of Affirmation Oil #5 on the bottom of each foot.

Speak Truth Affirmation: I have a sound mind. I am not confused or paralyzed by fear because I have an all-powerful, all-seeing, and loving Heavenly Father who is, at all times, protecting me, guiding my steps, and strengthening me.

Speak Affirmation Support:

- *For God has not given us a spirit of fear; but of power, and of love, and of a sound mind.* (2 Timothy 1:7)
- *God is not the author of confusion, but of peace.* (1 Corinthians 13:33)
- *Set your minds on things that are above, not on things that are on earth.* (Colossians 3:2)

JOURNAL PROMPT: What memories did God bring to your mind during this session? Write them down.

Ask the Lord to search you and reveal any toxic thoughts, memories, or trauma that He wants you to release to Him. Concentrate on becoming self-aware of your feelings and emotions: Anger? Shame? Sadness? Fear?

What emotions are you feeling? Where are you feeling them? When have you felt them before? Anoint yourself with your Prayer Oil by applying it directly to the place where you feel the emotion and ask the Lord to touch you—to heal you.

Ask God to also show you any bitterness or unforgiveness that you've harbored and forgive and release that, too.

Allow yourself to experience the pain or loss; but, this time, ponder the fact that Jesus was there with you the whole time, tenderly holding your soul and looking upon you with love and compassion, and looking ahead to your bright future.

How does that thought make you feel? Write out your experience and anything else the Lord shows you during this session. Pray and express your gratitude to God for what He is doing in you.

CHAPTER 7

Shame: Yours, Mine, or Ours?

I am chosen
Not forsaken
I am who You say I am.
You are for me
Not against me…
—Ben Fielding / Reuben Morgan

Rolling away from the morning sunlight that invaded the room, Shelly closed her eyes in protest. Out of habit, her hand stroked the spot where her husband used to sleep. The sheets felt empty and cold. When would the new normal begin?

Her head was foggy from another sleepless night and her mind began to wander, reliving that awful morning three weeks ago when her husband's confession had shot through her soul like a searing fire:

Shelly's eyes burned and her throat felt like it was closing. This wasn't happening. She leaned against the table to steady herself and finally found her voice. "When…what's her name?"

"It doesn't matter," Carl muttered, avoiding her eyes. "I don't love her. I…I don't love anyone. I just want out of this marriage. I feel like I'm suffocating. *You're* suffocating me."

"At least you're honest; you don't love anyone but yourself," she choked.

How could God have let this happen? She had read all the books, attended all the marriage seminars, supplied all his needs. She had listened to her pastor and tried to "win her husband without a word" by being more submissive, loving, and always available.

Sure, she hadn't always been perfect, but she had worked harder for this marriage than she'd worked for anything in her life. She racked her brain trying to figure out what she had done wrong—what was wrong with her. Self-deprecating thoughts invaded her mind.

Her worst nightmare was a reality. The warning signs had been there. The secretive behavior, the late nights, the anger, the coldness—she had known. But somehow hearing him say it out loud still took her breath away.

Now, here she was, three weeks later, facing the certainty of divorce and feeling like a part of her was dying. Shelly shook her head and wished away the haunting images of his detailed confession.

He didn't *want* her. She tried to swallow the bitterness of that reality, hoping that accepting it would ease the throbbing in her soul. Instead, her mind sifted through the mental file of personal inadequacies that she could blame: Ugly, fat, boring, plain. Over the next few months, that list would grow. What had she done wrong?

Shelly found herself wishing her husband would call and beg her forgiveness. How was it possible to ache for his embrace, while loathing the very thought of his touch? Her head hurt. Shelly glanced at the phone. What would she do if it rang? She knew.

HE LOVES ME NOT

Both the death of a spouse and infidelity or divorce leave us with feelings of grief, loss, and loneliness. With death, hopefully the sorrow is untainted, and the grief is free to flow. Unless there are other factors involved, a healthy grieving process can cleanse and heal the soul, so the memories can remain sweet.

But infidelity bitters all waters. Sexual and emotional betrayal are harshly personal—they ravage the soul like a violent assault. To complicate things, the unfaithfulness may be *retraumatizing*, specifically if a previous trauma is what contributed to what was likely already a dysfunctional relationship.

SOURCES OF SHAME

Whether our shame originated from adultery, sexual assault, abandonment, abuse, or even our own sin, its unique cruelty digs jagged claws into the heart, threatening to infect it with bitterness and hatred; even, and maybe especially, self-hatred. It leaves behind a permanent imprint—a tender battle scar that tells us we are somehow "unlovable."

Shame is wrapped up in how we view ourselves and, while there are many reasons why one may struggle with it, it is often rooted in having been rejected or assaulted in some way. It may also involve a fear that we are or will be rejected by God. A silent and insidious foe, shame torments the soul.

A shameful act was committed upon us. The perpetrator walked away, leaving us with the shame. We absorbed the notion that we are somehow defective. To cover for this, we constructed a false self, a masked self. And it is this self that is the overachiever or the dunce, the tramp or the puritan, the powermonger or the pathetic loser.
—Maureen Brady, *Beyond Survival: A Writing Journey for Healing Childhood Sexual Abuse*

If you suffer from lingering shame, you may find it difficult to even articulate the irrational thoughts that seem to chase you down in the dead of night or invade your mind unexpectedly during the day. If that's you, your feelings are real and valid, even if their authority over you is not. Yes, *you have a choice.*

THE SHADOW OF SHAME

Many of us struggle to get past our past. And I'm not just talking about things done by us, I'm also talking about things done to us. To make it even more confusing, it's usually all a little convoluted and jumbled together. We can repent of sins done by us, but when it's a shameful thing said or done to us—shame that we've *owned or internalized*, it's hard to shake, because they become linked in our mind.

Sometimes an abuse victim may learn to blame herself for her abuse, or even attach herself to or make excuses for and defend her abuser in what's called a "trauma bond."[16] Some of you know what I'm talking about. Have you ever felt guilty about or deserving of someone's poor treatment of you? Maybe you at least felt partially responsible.

Many times, we hide our shame, and drag it around like a ball and chain, as though it's something we asked for or deserved. We can't repent of it because it's not our sin, so we wind up in bondage to what I call the "shadow of shame." Yes, shame and fear often lurk in the shadows of our mind, rather than out in the open.

This is the kind of shame I struggled with. And, along the way, it became muddied by shameful things I actually *did*. So, in a way, shame became part of my identity—part of who I thought I was. I knew I was forgiven, that I was a new creation in Christ, but I still had inner shame that I felt obligated to own as a mark of my repentance and gratefulness to God.

I didn't call my abuse out for what it was, because I was convinced that I had brought it on myself somehow. I would say that I realized what the person did was wrong, but then I would excuse or minimize it by taking part of the blame.

So, throughout my life, I was the first to believe the worst about myself, as well as to assume others believed it, too. Kind of like putting yourself down first before someone else does. It's much easier to willingly *acknowledge* our own shame than to be a victim of it.

Like we learned earlier, if we grew up around someone who constantly criticized or shamed us, we will likely grow up with their voice in our head, and an obsessive desire to do all things "right" according to that voice. That's our inner effort to try make the voice stop.

Those are the brain habits that stick. It's as if every cell in our body remembers. In a very real way, that's exactly what is happening. Our body remembers all those feelings. Even if the memories themselves are

---

16   *The Betrayal Bond*, Patrick J. Carnes, PhD with Bonnie Phillips, PhD

forgotten, our body may remember the *feelings* of those memories. These are the brain habits we are breaking—the auto-responses that may have come from abuse or hurtful words.

> *"Emotions, though interpreted and named by the mind, are integrally an experience of the body."*—Babette Rothschild, *The Body Remembers*

IF THE SHOE DOESN'T FIT...

Another problem with shame is overcompensation. One way we may overcompensate is by taking on the guilt of another. There may indeed be times when we respond sinfully to someone's abusive behavior toward us, but that does not make us in any way responsible for their actions. Do not own someone else's guilt…even a little bit. Not only is it ineffective, it's also destructive to your (and their) mental health.

There were times when I willingly shared the blame for someone else's sin, imagining that it made it more likely for the other person to change. I even taught others to handle conflict this same way. I thought that by sharing the blame and admitting to things I had not done I could make it "easier" (or at least more likely) for the other person to see their own damaging behavior and change.

It was disingenuous and ineffective—a fruitless attempt in every way. In fact, it usually backfired and simply empowered those with abusive tendencies. Ironically, it was also a little prideful (and controlling). Somehow, I thought I could "handle" the guilt myself—theirs and mine—and fix it all my way.

AN ILLUSION OF A HAPPY HOME

To a child, the world needs to make sense—otherwise it's just too darn scary. When we're little, if our lives don't feel secure, we cope by convincing ourselves they are anyway. Moms and dads are supposed to nurture and protect their kids—to make them feel cherished, special, and safe; so, if for some reason they aren't, a child reasons that it must somehow be his fault—that there is something wrong with him.

It *can't* be that he is living in such a terrifying world that he's physically or emotionally unsafe in the assumably safest place there is! He convinces himself there must be something he's doing wrong—or worse, that there's something inherently wrong with him—something he lacks, something he could do better, and he sets out to fix it—to make the pain and fear go away…*his* way!

Somehow, that makes things feel less hopeless. Control. Those who try to cope in this way, convince themselves that if *they* can change—if they could just be a little bit better, a little bit smarter, and a little bit less annoying, the hurt will stop. In their minds, this ambiguous hope is better than none. So, they keep striving and failing.

One friend I knew grew up feeling like it was his responsibility to keep his dysfunctional mother "safe" from his father's wrath, so he strove to constantly appease his father and "keep the peace." This pattern trained his mind for future relationships.

Though he should have been the one to be protected and nurtured while growing up, he instead took on the role of emotional caregiver for his mother and siblings. As hard as he tried to single-handedly keep the family in one piece, pleasing his unpleasable father rarely worked. In the end, a child who is parentified in this way may convince himself that it's *all* hopeless—he will never be enough.

Most children are unable to face or verbalize their anger or sorrow about the loss of nurturing from their parent(s)… [they] suffer terrible loneliness and shame, having no idea how to deal with their losses except through self-blame and desperate attempts to restore the family's balance. Nancy Groom, *From Bondage to Bonding*

GOD SEES

To those struggling: There is One who knows *all* about your battle. He feels our suffering as if it's His own. He is well-acquainted with grief (Isaiah 53:3). He is El ro'i: "The God who sees me." He is not a far-off god; our God is a loving and intimate partner in our suffering.

He was there when it all began, counting our tears while shedding His own (Psalm 56:8). God even knows the illusive, faceless fears we dare not recollect—the memories our mind was merciful enough to block from us. He knows rejection, humiliation, and sorrow intimately.

> *He was despised and rejected by men, a man of sorrows*
> *and acquainted with grief…* (Isaiah 53:3)

You don't have to carry it. He already has. Jesus experienced great shame—*yours and mine*. He was there. He knows us better than we know ourselves (Psalm 139). He knows our fears, our loves, and the dark side of us we can't even face. He was there years ago when that pain settled into your soul, and He is empowering you now to overcome it (John 16:33).

> *Looking to Jesus, the founder and perfecter of our faith, who for the joy*
> *that was set before Him endured the cross, despising the shame, and is*
> *seated at the right hand of the throne of God…* (Hebrews 12:2)

He also knows *who we are* even if we don't yet know (1 Peter 2:9).

Jesus felt not only your shame and mine, but he also suffered the physical, emotional, and spiritual pain of the whole world when He bore our sins on the Cross. He suffered the rejection of the Father when sin separated them on our behalf. As Jesus was mocked, tortured, and hung naked until He died, He anticipated the *joy to come*—the victorious reunion with His Father and His redeemed Bride.

> *Satan doesn't care how we react to the sinfulness [shame] of abuse,*
> *as long as we don't turn to Jesus. The enemy knows that when*
> *we find our identity, security, and dignity in Christ, we can live in*
> *victory.*—Dawn Wilson, columnist for Crosswalk.com

So, the next time you're triggered by a painful experience, or even a reminder of your own failure, and shame tries to creep in, go ahead and *feel* it (don't stuff it). Only, instead of cowering under its weight or hiding, let it remind you of what Jesus did for you—of the magnitude of His love. Thank your loving Savior for taking that shame upon Himself. Let it sink in…then let it go. It's not yours to bear.

> *He himself bore our sins in His body on the tree, that we might die to sin and live*
> *to righteousness. By His wounds you have been healed.* (1 Peter 2:24)

TRUTH DROP SESSION WEEK 7

Shame

Inhale the Truth and Exhale the Lies

Practice all the steps below every morning
and every evening for one week.

Shame is one of the most crippling and damaging of all emotions and, to some degree, we probably all struggle with some form of it. The shame that attempts to lord over us must bow to the name of Jesus. Fear and shame have no authority or claim over us, so we need to stop submitting to their voices.

If it originated from what someone did to us, Jesus protects us and reminds us of our great worth in His sight. If it originated from what we ourselves did wrong, He offers us forgiveness and restoration; again, reminding us of how much He values us. It's all about who He is, what He did for us, and what His thoughts are toward us.

Breathe deeply, as you reflect, meditate, and embrace the meaning of each Truth Drop, and internalize the reality of who God is and what He says about you.

Anoint your forehead, temples, and brainstem with your Chosen Prayer Oil and pray:

Lord, I can trust You because You are good, You are perfect, You are all all-powerful, You are holy, You love me, and You know me better than any other. You have redeemed me and called me your own!

Help me to walk in the truth of your love simply because I know it's true, even on days that I don't feel it. Help me to see my life, and even my past pain, as a gift to be redeemed—to embrace my past and my suffering as something valuable that will be transformed into something that will glorify You and to help me grow stronger.

In Jesus' Name, Amen

1. TRUTH DROPS

Anoint: Apply 1-3 drops of Affirmation Oil #1 on each wrist.

Speak Truth Affirmation: God's Word is 100% true, and it is my guide to what God thinks about me; therefore, I choose to listen to and believe His voice above all others. I am not in bondage to the toxic voices of my past, and I choose not to listen to or entertain them when they attempt to whisper their lies or to hold me back from moving forward in life.

The Lord has given me beauty for ashes and transformed my weeping into joy and worship. I have laid down my spirit of heaviness and gladly received His joy. I choose life, rather than death. I have been consoled. I am filled with beauty and joy. I am planted by the Lord right where I need to be.

Speak Affirmation Support:
- *All Scripture is given by inspiration of God.* (2 Timothy 3:16)
- *Your word is a lamp to my feet and a light to my path.* (Psalm 119:105)
- *To console those who mourn in Zion, to give them beauty for ashes, the oil of joy for mourning, the garment of praise for the spirit of heaviness; that they may be called trees of righteousness, the planting of the Lord, that He may be glorified.* (Isaiah 61:3)

2. TRUTH DROPS

Anoint: Apply 1-3 drops of Affirmation Oil #2 to the back of the neck.

Speak Truth Affirmation: When I am afraid of what others think of me, I will remember that it is only God's opinion that matters—the God in whose very image I am made—the God who gave His own Son as a sacrifice for me! I will revere only God.

Even when people fail me, I will trust God to take care of me. He is always faithful, and He loves me. He has always been with me, even when I didn't know it. He orchestrates my steps. I don't need to worry about what people think or say about me because the God of Heaven is on *my* side.

Speak Affirmation Support:
- *The fear of man brings a snare, but whoever trusts in the Lord shall be safe.* (Proverbs 29:25)
- *I, even I, am He who comforts you. Who are you that you should be afraid of a man who will die, and of the son of a man who will be made like grass?* (Isaiah 51:12)
- *Rescue me, Oh my God, from the hand of the wicked, from the grasp of the unjust and cruel man. For you, Oh Lord, are my hope, my trust, Oh Lord, from my youth.* (Psalm 71:4-5)

3. TRUTH DROPS
Anoint: Apply 1-3 drops of Affirmation Oil #3 over the heart.

Speak Truth Affirmation: I am created to be exactly who God wants me to be. I am valued, I am loved, and I am chosen by God. He orchestrates my steps. He has stored every tear I've shed; none of my pain is wasted and none of my past shame is uncovered. I am clothed in His righteousness! I am washed clean, and I'm a new creation in Christ!

When I am weak, He provides me with His strength to do what He calls me to do.

Speak Affirmation Support:
- *I can do all things through Christ who strengthens me.* (Philippians 4:13)
- *He who has begun a good work in you will complete it until the day of Jesus Christ...* (Philippians 1:6)
- *O my God, in You I trust...none who wait for You shall be put to shame...* (Psalm 25:2)

4. TRUTH DROPS
Anoint: Apply 1-3 drops of Affirmation Oil #4 to the edges of each ear.

Speak Truth Affirmation: Any loss I have suffered will be replaced to overflowing by His Spirit. When I ask the Lord to fill the voids in my soul with His healing power, He is faithful in doing it because He loves me....

I have lived through a lot, but I know that God loves me, and He won't waste any of my pain. He is healing me, strengthening me, and using all of it for my good and His glory. No one else gets to define who I am. Only God does! I will speak life and kindness over myself and my loved ones.

Speak Affirmation Support:
- *Those who look to Him are radiant, and their faces shall never be ashamed.* (Psalm 34:5)
- *Do not fear, for you will not be ashamed; neither be disgraced, for you will not be put to shame; for you will forget the shame of your youth...* (Isaiah 54:4)
- *Instead of your shame there shall be a double portion; instead of dishonor they shall rejoice in their lot...they shall have everlasting joy.* (Isaiah 61:7)

5. TRUTH DROPS

Anoint: Apply 1-3 drops of Affirmation Oil #5 on the bottom of each foot.

Speak Truth Affirmation: The Lord has forgiven my true shame—shame that resulted from my own sin. But I will no longer accept or carry the shame that came from the sins of others. The Lord is my rescuer—He is my refuge. I will not be ashamed.

Speak Affirmation Support:
- *To You they cried and were rescued; in You they trusted and were not put to shame.* (Psalm 22:5)
- *Oh, guard my soul, and deliver me! Let me not be put to shame, for I take refuge in You.* (Psalm 25:20)
- *Everyone who believes in Him will not be put to shame.* (Romans 10:11)

JOURNAL PROMPT: What memories did God bring to your mind during this session? Write them down.

Ask the Lord to search you and reveal any toxic thoughts, memories, or trauma that He wants you to release to Him. Concentrate on becoming self-aware of your feelings and emotions: Anger? Shame? Sadness? Fear?

What emotions are you feeling? Where are you feeling them? When have you felt them before? Anoint yourself with your Prayer Oil by applying it directly to the place where you feel the emotion and ask the Lord to touch you—to heal you.

Ask God to also show you any bitterness or unforgiveness that you've harbored and forgive and release that, too.

Allow yourself to experience the pain or loss; but, this time, ponder the fact that Jesus was there with you the whole time, tenderly holding your soul and looking upon you with love and compassion, and looking ahead to your bright future.

How does that thought make you feel? Write out your experience and anything else the Lord shows you during this session. Pray and express your gratitude to God for what He is doing in you.

CHAPTER 8

"Neither Do I Condemn You"

Not only are guilt feelings destructive, they are diametrically opposed to a scriptural view of motivation and actually reflect our own independent efforts to solve the problem of sin in our lives. They actually pose a barrier to spiritual growth and maturity rather than being an incentive for it.—S. Bruce Narramore

There is a legitimate time to feel guilty. When we sin, God may convict us in our spirit that what we did was wrong or hurtful, so that we know to turn from it and turn to Jesus. Even a young child may feel the sting of guilt when he steals, lies, or hurts someone else. God's Word says the law is written on our hearts (Romans 2:15), so we all have an internal sense of justice.

But sometimes, either because of trauma, manipulation, or even warped theology, our sense of guilt is distorted. When our perception becomes convoluted, the Enemy can use it as a weapon to torment us—leaving us perpetually fearful and with a sense of constant judgment in our spirit. This can lead to hypervigilance and anxiety, as well as legalism.

1 John 1:9 says that if we confess our sins to Jesus, He is "faithful and just to forgive us our sins and to cleanse us from all unrighteousness." So why do we continue to beat ourselves up? Why do we so often have difficulty forgiving ourselves even after Jesus forgives us?

If Jesus took our sins upon Himself at the Cross and chose to forgive us, why can't we seem to let go of the guilt? Could it be that we're in a sort of mind-bondage because of thought patterns established in the past— brain habits that developed over time, which now resemble an addiction of sorts—an addiction to *guilt*?

The Book of Romans is not primarily a book telling us how to gain eternal life (i.e., be saved from Hell). It is telling us how to live a righteous life. After we become believers, we still live in this physical body that can and does sin. If we walk by the flesh, we can still be slaves to the power of sin. But we don't have to do that. Through the Spirit, we can be set free from the "condemnation" of this slavery.[17]

Remember, conviction and condemnation are two very separate things. Conviction comes from the Holy Spirit and firmly points us to the Gospel—to a *real solution* beyond ourselves. Condemnation comes from the Enemy and exclusively points not to us, but *at us*! In order to torment the child of God, the Enemy tries to make any sort of solution or relief seem elusive and out of reach.

To a repentant Believer who is walking "in the flesh" in this way (bad brain habits), the Enemy uses condemnation (slavery to sin) to whisper lies and confusion, telling him his repentance isn't enough. And, if he is pre-conditioned to doubt his own value and question his own judgment of reality, he unnecessarily walks in constant punishment, as one who is destined for Hell. He unnecessarily suffers the consequences of a death sentence that isn't his. Jesus came so that we might walk in freedom *starting now*!

If the Son makes you free, you shall be free indeed. (John 8:36)

SIN ACCORDING TO GRACE

The miraculous solution to condemnation is mercy, and the only meaningful mercy comes from the Lover of our Soul—the One who sees through our sin and looks upon us with love, compassion, and Heavenly Grace. He is our example. Because Jesus, the only One who was without sin, forgave those of us who were drowning in it, we can view those who have sinned against us through that same lens of mercy.

As Believers, when we walk with a spirit of compassion, forgiveness, and mercy for ourselves and others, the Enemy *loses his power over us*. When we walk in the spirit (Galatians 5:18, 25), the only one left for the Enemy to point to is He who became sin on our behalf (2 Corinthians 5:21).

---

17   Ken Yates, Editor of the *Journal of the Grace Evangelical Society and the pastor of Little River Baptist Church in Jenkinsville, SC.*

THE FIRST STONE

Consider the woman described in the Gospel of John chapter 8, caught in the very act of adultery. I've often wondered what the details of that traumatic scene of judgment and confrontation must have been, and why wasn't the man with whom she was committing adultery seized and dragged to the scene as well?

In fact, the Scribes and Pharisees conveniently left out important details of the Law when they tried to corner Jesus: "Moses commanded us to stone such women. So what do you say?" (John 8:5)

In reality, the Law said that "if a man commits adultery with the wife of his neighbor, *both* the adulterer *and* the adulteress shall surely be put to death" (Leviticus 20:10, emphasis mine).

So where was he...the missing half of this adulterous equation? And what were those mysteriously convicting words that Jesus so calmly wrote in the sand—words that caused the condemning crowd to silently drop their stones and wander away one by one?

Jesus answered the woman's accusers, "Let him who is without sin among you be the first to throw a stone at her" (John 8:7). Those words must have hung in the air.

> *And once more he bent down and wrote on the ground. But when they heard it, they went away one by one, beginning with the older ones, and Jesus was left alone with the woman standing before him.* (John 8:8-9)

Can you imagine the raw emotion in that moment—the sounds, the smells, the sight of it all? The silent shock on this devastated woman's face? Her heart pounding, her heavy sobs, her own sweat mixed with tears? The overwhelming gratitude in her eyes when Jesus stood up and locked her gaze with His and said, "Neither do I condemn you; go, and from now on sin no more" (John 8:11). Jesus set an unprecedented example of mercy for us all that day.

FORGIVING THE UNFORGIVABLE

When considering whether or not you can forgive those who have hurt you, also consider those who you may have hurt in other ways. Do you really want to pick up that stone? "For with the same measure that you use, it will be measured back to you" (Luke 6:38, NKJV).

For clarification, I'm talking about heart-forgiveness, which doesn't always include physical reconciliation. I sometimes wonder if we struggle to forgive *ourselves* because the Enemy has us in bondage to bitterness and unforgiveness against someone else. Subconsciously, we know there is some sort of cognitive dissonance going on, so our minds try to make it all consistent. In the process, we punish ourselves along with our abuser(s).

> *Though your sins are like scarlet, they shall be as white as snow; though they are red like crimson, they shall be as wool.* (Isaiah 1:18)

Maybe you never suffered sexual or physical abuse, but you were raised by an emotionally abusive or harsh parent. The result could still be lingering thoughts that make you feel constantly judged, condemned, or worthless. This too can cause self-blame, insecurity, and feelings of defeat and condemnation.

DEBTS AND DEBTORS

Matthew 18:21-35 tells the story of a servant who was in debt to his master for 10,000 denarii. He was about to be thrown in prison because he couldn't pay the debt, but he begged for mercy, so the master was moved with compassion and forgave the *entire* debt!

Afterward, it wasn't long before the forgiven servant came across a fellow servant who owed him just 100 denarii—a fraction of what he had just been forgiven. But instead of offering his friend the same mercy he had just received, he had him thrown into prison.

When the Master heard about it, he was appalled and told the unmerciful servant that because he was unwilling to forgive his fellow servant as he had been forgiven, that he was to be *tormented* until his own debt was paid. This concept of "forgiving debts/offenses" is even highlighted in the Lord's prayer: "Forgive us our debts and we forgive our debtors."

So the part that really got me thinking here was the word "torment" in verse 34. Would you agree that guilt and shame are a form of torture or *torment* to the mind and soul? That's why the Devil is often called the accuser—he's attempting to *torment* us by constantly reminding us of our sin and the (voided/redeemed) condemnation we deserve.

Remember, the Devil knows the Word of God, too, so he knows that if he can keep us in bondage to our bitterness, he can and will torment us with it. As Believers, he can't *steal our soul*, but he can try to *steal our joy*, as well as the productive and abundant life we have inherited!

The thief does not come except to steal, and to kill, and to destroy. I have come that they may have life, and that they may have it more abundantly. (John 10:10)

Now, to be clear, when I talk about forgiveness, again, I'm not necessarily talking about reconciling with the person or people who have hurt you—or even maintaining any sort of relationship. You don't have to be best buds. Sometimes, it's not wise, safe, or even an option to reconcile or even be in the same room with the person.

I'm also not necessarily talking about *feelings* of forgiveness or affection. It can be normal to feel hurt, fear, and even righteous anger. I'm talking about *choosing* to forgive and release—the peaceful feelings may come later. "Bless those who curse you and pray for those who spitefully use [abuse] you." (Luke 6:28)

It would be great if the person who wronged us repented and apologized, but whether or not that ever happens, we can forgive and release them. We are talking about our own mental and spiritual health; we cannot control or change others. This can be difficult when the feelings are painful and raw, but it's important for moving forward.

Cry out to God and ask Him to do a work in your spirit—to liberate you from the bondage of fear, resentment, and bitterness. Trust Him to renew your mind and heal your heart. Then move on to also forgive yourself. Untangle and release the false beliefs and chronic condemnation that has caused you so much pain and confusion.

"To forgive is to set a prisoner free and discover that the prisoner was you."[18]

The Bible says to resist the Devil and he will flee! Stop listening to His impotent ramblings; you are a child of the King of Kings and "He who is in you is greater than he who is in the world" (1 John 4:4).

As badly as we may have been hurt, if we refuse to forgive, and we hold onto bitterness, aren't we "walking in the flesh?" Isn't that what *anyone* would do? The "flesh" is all wrapped up in the Law, punishment, and worldly justice (leading to death). "Walking in the spirit" is all about God's supernatural love, mercy, and grace (abundant life)! If we walk in the flesh, in a way, we walk in self-imposed torment.

SPIRITUAL SELF-HARM

Do you know there are still Christians today who believe in the practice of self-flagellation?[19] They literally beat themselves with whips as a form of "penance" and in a vain attempt to demonstrate their remorse for their sin. They attempt to add their own distorted self-martyrdom to the ultimate ransom of Christ.

In a way, it's a form of pride and arrogance dressed up as humility. As if we can out-sacrifice what Jesus did for us so freely and completely on the Cross! This practice of sacred self-harm was much more common with Roman Catholic monks in early centuries, but it's still practiced by some sects today.[20]

Willingly submitting to abuse, whether it is self-inflicted or permitted mistreatment from someone else, does not communicate humility, devotion, or godliness. It communicates delusion. In a way, when we punish ourselves emotionally with self-deprecatory thoughts or we live out self-imposed gnostic philosophies, we are doing the same thing. It doesn't breed godliness; it breeds contempt.

---

18   Lewis B. Smedes, *Forgive and Forget: Healing the Hurts We Don't Deserve*
19   "Flagellants." *The Oxford Dictionary of the Christian Church.* Edited by F. L. Cross and E. A. Livingstone. Oxford, 1997.
20   http://news.bbc.co.uk/2/hi/uk_news/magazine/8375174.stm

IT STARTS NOW

Have you put your faith in Christ and asked Him to forgive you? If not, then do it now. But if you have already asked for forgiveness, "there is therefore now no condemnation to those who are in Christ Jesus, who do not walk according to the flesh, but according to the Spirit" (Romans 8:1, NKJV).

Claim it, believe it, and *walk in it*! Jesus came to set the captives free! "For God so loved the world, that he gave his only Son, that whoever believes in him should not perish but have eternal life" (John 3:16).

We don't have to live in bondage to *anything*! I recommend that you read and meditate on all of Romans 8 this week. Remember, a day is coming when He will wipe away *every tear*! There will be no more death or mourning or crying or pain (Revelations 21:4). Abundant life starts now!

Let us then with confidence draw near to the throne of grace, that we may receive mercy and find grace to help in time of need. (Hebrews 4:16)

TRUTH DROP SESSION WEEK 8
False Guilt, Condemnation, Legalism

Inhale the Truth and Exhale the Lies

Practice all the steps below every morning
and every evening for one week.

What we think about God matters…a LOT. You may have heard
people say they don't need theology; they just need Jesus. But theology
is literally the "study of God." So, we all have some sort of theology
we believe. It impacts what we think about God, and how we think He
views us. And this understanding can change everything.

We can dress up a devil in a robe and call Him Jesus, but heart and soul,
he's still a devil—an imposter (Colossians 2:8, 2 John 1:7-8)! So, we need
to know the difference. Many people are in bondage to false religions
and false realities, as well as false perceptions of God and themselves.
Use this week to explore the character and attributes of God. Do you
view your Heavenly Father as attentive, tender, and merciful toward His
children? Or do you see Him as aloof, stern, and cruel?

Breathe deeply as you reflect, meditate, and embrace the meaning of
each Truth Drop, and internalize the reality of who God is and what He
says about you.

Anoint your forehead, temples, and brainstem with your Chosen Prayer
Oil and pray:

*Heavenly Father, please pour out your Holy Spirit upon me today. Bring healing to my
heart—restore my soul and renew my mind. Help me to reject the lies of the Enemy—
lies that would keep me in bondage to the mind and the flesh, and that accuse me
day and night. Help me to instead embrace the sweet aroma of Your Living Word.*

Thank you for your mercy and forgiveness. Help me to be at peace, Lord. Help me to keep my mind continually focused on You. Help me to forgive and release any bitterness or resentment I have buried and to extend mercy to those who are in bondage to their sin. Please give me discernment and clarity of mind to know how to set appropriate boundaries and still bless others. Help me to remember all You've done for me. Thank you, Lord.

In Jesus' Name, Amen.

1. TRUTH DROPS

Anoint: Apply 1-3 drops of Affirmation Oil #1 on each wrist.

Speak Truth Affirmation: Jesus set me free the moment I put my trust in Him. I cling to His Word, and I walk in the truth of my rightful freedom. Nothing can separate me from the endless, extravagant love of my Heavenly Father, through my Lord and Savior, Jesus Christ.

I will not submit to the slavery of sin or false guilt. I am free because of Jesus, and I will stand firm in His mercy, love and grace! He carries my burdens. I am forgiven. I am set free. I am a survivor.

Speak Affirmation Support:
- *If you abide in My word, you are truly My disciples, and you will know the truth, and the truth will set you free… If the Son sets you free, you will be free indeed.* (John 8:31-32, 36)
- *Who shall separate us from the love of Christ? Shall tribulation, or distress, or persecution, or famine, or nakedness, or danger, or sword?… No, in all these things we are more than conquerors through him who loved us. For I am sure that neither death nor life, nor angels nor rulers, nor things present nor things to come, nor powers, nor height nor depth, nor anything else in all creation, will be able to separate us from the love of God in Christ Jesus our Lord.* (Romans 8:35, 37-39)
- *For freedom Christ has set us free; stand firm therefore, and do not submit again to a yoke of slavery.* (Galatians 5:1)

2. TRUTH DROPS

Anoint: Apply 1-3 drops of Affirmation Oil #2 to the back of the neck.

Speak Truth Affirmation: I reject the false guilt and judgment of the world and grieve only for my own real sin. I am bought with the blood of Jesus! I am a redeemed daughter/son of the King of Kings. Because of His finished work on the Cross, I am cleansed, forgiven, and pure in the sight of my Heavenly Father.

Speak Affirmation Support:
- *For godly grief produces a repentance that leads to salvation without regret, whereas worldly grief produces death.* (2 Corinthians 7:10)
- *He was wounded for our transgressions, He was bruised for our iniquities: the chastisement of our peace was upon Him; and with His stripes we are healed.* (Isaiah 53:5)
- *The Lord is merciful and gracious, slow to anger, and abounding in mercy.* (Psalm 103:8)

3. TRUTH DROPS
Anoint: Apply 1-3 drops of Affirmation Oil #3 over the heart.

Speak Truth Affirmation: I am secure in my salvation because the God of Heaven has redeemed me. I will not own guilt that belongs to others, and I will not carry my guilt that Jesus already paid for. I am forgiven by God, and I forgive myself. The Lord has compassion on me.

He has created me with a purpose to fulfill—a future of healing and hope. He has called me to impact lives for good, to love like He loved, and to glorify Him with all that I am. The Lord is my help and strength.

Speak Affirmation Support:
- *The accuser of our brothers has been thrown down, who accuses them day and night before our God.* (Revelations 12:10)
- *Neither do I condemn you; go, and from now on sin no more.* (John 8:11)
- *With everlasting love I will have compassion on you.* (Isaiah 54:8)

4. TRUTH DROPS
Anoint: Apply 1-3 drops of Affirmation Oil #4 to the edges of each ear.

Speak Truth Affirmation: I willingly drop my stone in the dirt and, because Christ forgave me, I forgive those who hurt me. I freely release to God all bitterness, resentment, and animosity. As Christ forgave me, I forgive those who hurt me—those who are in bondage to the misery of their sin.

I am walking in peace, truth, and patience. I am thankful for all that God has done for me, and I want others to experience that same freedom. God is faithful! I am free. I am strong. I am abounding in goodness, love, and truth. My heart is at peace with those who have hurt me. I am forgiving and forgiven.

Speak Affirmation Support:
- *If it is possible, as much as depends on you, live peaceably with all men.* (Romans 12)
- *For with the same measure that you use, it will be measured back to you.* (Luke 6:38, NKJV)
- *This I recall to my mind; therefore, I have hope. Through the Lord's mercies we are not consumed, because His compassions fail not. They are new every morning; great is Your faithfulness...* (Lamentations 3:21-24)

5. TRUTH DROPS
Anoint: Apply 1-3 drops of Affirmation Oil #5 on the bottom of each foot.

Speak Truth Affirmation: I am loved by the Creator of the Universe, and He has equipped me with His strength and the power to overcome my anxieties! My healthy thoughts are clear and unwavering. I am free to give and receive love from God and from others. The Lord is always with me; even when I don't sense His presence, He is there. He constantly helps and supports me.

I reject false guilt. I am steadfast, determined, and confident in who I am in Christ. I have been forgiven and redeemed. He is my vindicator, my shield, my helper, and my Savior. I am secure. I am steady. I am loved.

Speak Affirmation Support:
- *For he who touches you touches the apple of His eye...* (Zechariah 2:8)
- *Finally, be strong in the Lord and in the strength of his might. Put on the*

whole armor of God, that you may be able to stand against the schemes of the devil. (Ephesians 6:10-11)

- *There is no fear in love; but perfect love casts out fear, because fear involves torment. But he who fears has not been made perfect in love.* (1 John 4:18)

JOURNAL PROMPT: What memories did God bring to your mind during this session? Write them down.

Ask the Lord to search you and reveal any toxic thoughts, memories, or trauma that He wants you to release to Him. Concentrate on becoming self-aware of your feelings and emotions: Anger? Shame? Sadness? Fear?

What emotions are you feeling? Where are you feeling them? When have you felt them before? Anoint yourself with your Prayer Oil by applying it directly to the place where you feel the emotion and ask the Lord to touch you—to heal you.

Ask God to also show you any bitterness or unforgiveness that you've harbored and forgive and release that, too.

Allow yourself to experience the pain or loss; but, this time, ponder the fact that Jesus was there with you the whole time, tenderly holding your soul and looking upon you with love and compassion, and looking ahead to your bright future.

How does that thought make you feel? Write out your experience and anything else the Lord shows you during this session. Pray and express your gratitude to God for what He is doing in you.

CHAPTER 9

Abundant Living

*The danger is not that we should fall…but that we should
remain on the ground.*—John Chrysostom

While I was in labor during my first homebirth, my midwife filled
a heated crockpot with water, washcloths, and a combination of
frankincense and lavender oil. During each contraction, my husband
laid one of the steamy cloths across my belly. Temporarily, the pain
seemed to melt and the intoxicating aroma of essential oils filled the air
and helped me to relax.

One of the best bits of advice I received during labor came from my
midwife, and I've found it useful in every other area of life:

> *Don't waste the pain. Push into it. You're going to have to experience it anyway, so
> you may as well make it productive. If you hide from it or avoid it, you'll just prolong
> the pain—you'll give it power over you and it will seem even worse than it is.*

Although I could still *feel* the contraction, I deliberately focused on the
heat from the cloth over my belly, as well as the scent of the powerful
essential oils. The concept of pain seemed to change, making it more
manageable. As I concentrated on my senses of smell and touch, I found
myself able to control my breathing all the way through the contraction.

Instead of running from the pain, which would have been
counterproductive, I pushed into it, helping the baby to move closer
to being born—so that the pain would end and the fruit of my labors
would come to pass!

Having embraced the whole idea of natural childbirth during my first
pregnancy, I learned right away that if I was going to avoid drugs, I

needed to find other ways to cope with the pain of labor. Sometimes that meant pushing into the pain, rather than running from it. The same is true in other areas of life.

An insightful pastor said in a sermon recently, "Focus on your purpose and you'll lose sight of your fears; focus on your fears and you'll lose sight of your purpose."[21] We grant incredible power in our lives to whatever we give reverence or attention. If you've been consuming too much gloom and doom lately, this should give you pause.

LIFE ABOVE THE WAVES

Living in a fallen world, we are sure to face all sorts of pain in life. Jesus warned us about this when He told us to take heart and be at peace, because He overcame it all—that He is ultimately in charge (John 16:33). We can't avoid pain, but through Christ, we can refuse its power over us.

Pushing into the pain doesn't mean we seek it out; it means we don't cower or run from it in fear. We boldly move forward with Christ as our strength. We recognize that God is orchestrating the details of our lives and we learn to trust that He has our ultimate good in mind. He is writing our story, and He is an excellent author (Hebrews 12:2, NKJV).

In addition, the answer isn't to simply try harder or to conjure up more faith. That's still trying to do things our way and in our own strength. So where can we tap into this power source of faith?

Lord...help my unbelief (Mark 9:24)!

Lord, increase my faith (Luke 17:5)!

Lord, give me the strength I need (Isaiah 40:29)!

Ephesians 2:8 reveals that we depend upon *Him* even for our faith. Jesus said that His yoke is easy, and His burden is light. He was the contrasting spiritual simplicity of our faith in Him with the bondage and weight of striving with the law—the heavy burden we've been lugging around.

---

21   Cal Rychener, Northwoods Community Church, Peoria, IL

As we *follow*, Jesus leads and carries us. He never said the burden itself was light; He wanted to show us that we don't have the strength to carry such a burden without Him! His yoke—His *leading*, is a refreshing load off our shoulders, because we know God is in control. As we follow and rely on Him, we learn to walk in the "lightness" and joy of faith!

> *He gives power to the weak, and to those who have no might He increases strength.* (Isaiah 40:29)

In Matthew Henry's commentary on Peter, we read that Jesus trained the Disciples up "by degrees to live by faith, and not by sense."[22] That's what He's doing with us. Just as we train up our children by degrees, God trains us to walk in the spirit (His way), rather than in the flesh (our way). Jesus is with us in the midst of every one of our storms.

I needed to stop trusting my outdated coping mechanisms and start actively turning to Jesus for my protection, connection, and validation. When we bond with the Holy Spirit, we are securely attached indeed.

DOING IT SCARED

Consider Peter's experience in the book of Matthew on that windy night with the waves crashing against the side of the boat. Peter was a real man with real fears and emotions, just like us. Imagine the sound of the wind—the feel and taste of the salty spray slapping him in the face.

In his flesh, he had to be afraid, but he fixed his gaze on Jesus, His Lord. Imagine the exhilaration in that passionate moment when Jesus commanded Peter to step out of the boat and walk upon the threatening waves toward Him? Can you picture the intensity? Have you ever wondered why Jesus didn't just calm the storm first, so that it wouldn't be so scary for Peter? He could have made the whole scene a story of serenity and ease.

There have literally been times when I've asked God to make things less scary. But sometimes He wants us to "do it scared," while trusting Him. It's only in the trusting that it gets less scary. Jesus doesn't hand us a life

---

22   Matthew Henry's *Commentary on the Whole Bible, The Book of Matthew*, *vs 22–33.*

jacket before He calls us to walk. He *is* our life jacket! He called Peter to step out in faith and action during and despite the turbulence! Peter was in training, and so are we.

You keep Him in perfect peace whose mind is stayed on you, because He trusts in you. (Isaiah 26:3)

And, as crazy as it must have felt, Peter took that first move of faith and stepped out of the boat. He did it! But look what happened next: "But when he saw the wind, he was afraid, and beginning to sink he cried out, 'Lord, save me.'"

TURN YOUR EYES

It probably wasn't Peter's finest moment. And it's recorded for all of history to see (and relate to). When he took his *eyes off Jesus* and instead *focused on the wind*, the storm stole Peter's attention, and Jesus entered his peripheral vision (became blurry). Peter immediately began to fear...and to sink.

Turn your eyes upon Jesus
Look full in His wonderful face
And the things of earth will grow strangely dim
In the light of His glory and grace.[23]

But notice (and this is important) Jesus didn't abandon him. He didn't say, "Well, now you've blown it! You brought this on yourself! You deserve to sink!" When Peter cried out to Jesus, "Lord, save me!" Jesus saved him.

Jesus immediately reached out his hand, took firm hold of Peter, and with affection and tender rebuke, said, "O you of little faith, why did you doubt?" (Matthew 14:31) There is so much power and meaning wrapped up in those words. "Don't you know I love you?" "Do you realize how much power I have?" "Don't you know I'll protect you?" "After all this time, how can you not trust Me?" "Don't you know how much *you mean to Me?*"

---

23   Helen Howarth Lemmel, *Turn Your Eyes Upon Jesus, (1922)*

If you are a parent, you've probably experienced holding your precious little child in the deep end of the pool, consoling their fears, as they cling to you with all their might. "Why do you doubt me, sweetheart? Mommy has you." As if you'd just let them sink to the bottom of the pool!

Do you find your perception of God changing? If so, could it be that you've sometimes viewed God through the lens of trauma, rather than truth?

Be strong and courageous. Do not be frightened, and do not be dismayed, for the Lord your God is with you wherever you go. (Joshua 1:9)

Keep your eyes off the wind and lock eyes with the One who controls it. Keep your mind off the waves and focus on the One who walks on it. Ignore the lies (who the Enemy says you are) and listen intently to the Truth (who God says you are).

God wants us to remember our identity in Christ. And He wants us to learn to trust who He is, as well as to believe and experience His love for us. He's never going to let one of His children sink. "He Himself has said, 'I will never leave you nor forsake you'" (Hebrews 13:5). Even if God doesn't change our situation, He will give us what we need to persevere through it.

When I look back over the years to the numerous times He protected me and spared my life, even way back before I knew or loved Him in return, I can clearly see that *even then* He knew me—He loved me—He chose me to be His own child (Ephesians 1:4–6).

I have named you, though you have not known Me. (Isaiah 45:4, NKJV)

Even as I tried to hide from all the pain, and I clung to my sin and despair, my Savior was there drawing me, wooing me, calling me. In fact, He wrote my name on His hand (Isaiah 49:16), He covered my shame, and He protected me from destruction. So why in the world would I think He would let me down now? How could I ever have doubted Him? From the beginning, He is the One who held me fast—my rock!

The Lord is my rock and my fortress and my deliverer, my God, my rock, in whom I take refuge, my shield, and the horn of my salvation, my stronghold and my refuge, my Savior... (2 Samuel 22:2-3)

Sweet friend, you are the apple of God's eye (Deuteronomy 32:10). Cling tightly to Him, as He holds you in the deep end. But also learn to trust that He won't let you sink, as he trains you by degrees to get out of the boat—to get past your past and to move forward in hope!

For I know the plans I have for you, declares the Lord, plans for welfare and not for evil, to give you a future and a hope. (Jeremiah 29:11)

TRUTH DROP SESSION WEEK 9
The Abundant Life

Inhale the Truth and Exhale the Lies

Practice all the steps below every morning
and every evening for one week.

Remember, in this life, we are not healed; we are healing! So, internalizing Truth Drops should be a life-long practice. But, even in the process of healing, Jesus has given us life—*abundant life*! We grow, heal, and enjoy Him and each other in the process!

I hope you have noticed progress and healing, as you've worked through these exercises. God's Word does not return void (Isaiah 55:11), so regularly speaking His truth over yourself (the Word He sent forth) will always be productive. During times when you are tempted to doubt, cry out to Him to supply whatever it is you lack. He is always faithful!

Breathe deeply, as you reflect, meditate, and embrace the meaning of each Truth Drop, and internalize the reality of who God is and what He says about you.

Anoint your forehead, temples, and brainstem with your Chosen Prayer Oil and pray:

Lord, please help me to feel what I know to be true in my heart—that You are my certainty. Please help my unbelief, increase my faith, and give me the strength I need! Help me to keep my eyes on you in the midst of any storm of life.

Help me to remember that you have everything under control, regardless of how crazy it looks on my end. Help me to trust You and to walk boldly in peace and confidence, knowing that you will not let me sink. Strengthen my soul and shine Your light through me, so that I might boldly spread Your peace and healing in a hurting world.

In Jesus' Name, Amen

1. TRUTH DROPS

Anoint: Apply 1-3 drops of Affirmation Oil #1 on each wrist.

Speak Truth Affirmation: God is near, and He comforts me when I call out to Him. I am fulfilled and satisfied in every way. Any time I need Him, God hears my cry and saves me. He is nourishing and renewing my soul. I am growing. I am at peace. I am safe. I am getting stronger each day.

Speak Affirmation Support:
- *Fear not, for I am with you; be not dismayed, for I am your God; I will strengthen you, I will help you, I will uphold you with my righteous right hand.* (Isaiah 41:10)
- *The Lord is near to all who call on Him, to all who call on Him in truth. He fulfills the desire of those who fear Him; He also hears their cry and saves them.* (Psalm 145:18-19)
- *You keep him in perfect peace whose mind is stayed on You, because He trusts in you.* (Isaiah 26:3)

2. TRUTH DROPS

Anoint: Apply 1-3 drops of Affirmation Oil #2 on the back of the neck.

Speak Truth Affirmation: God is in control of the future—of *my* future. Just as a great composer creates a masterpiece, God is orchestrating the details of my life. One day, I will see with my own eyes the great harmony of it all. But whether God shows me the details or not, I will trust Him.

I will only carry what God gives me to carry. The rest I will trust Him to bear. He is leading the way and He gives me rest. It is not "all up to me." God is in control. I am content. I am unburdened. I am covered.

Speak Affirmation Support:
- *The heart of man plans his way, but the Lord establishes his steps.* (Proverbs 16:9)
- *Come to me, all who labor and are heavy laden, and I will give you rest. Take My yoke upon you, and learn from Me, for I am gentle and lowly in heart,*

and you will find rest for your souls. For My yoke is easy, and My burden is light. (Matthew 11:28-30)
- *He Himself has said, "I will never leave you nor forsake you."* (Hebrews 13:5)

3. TRUTH DROPS

Anoint: Apply 1-3 drops of Affirmation Oil #3 on the chest, over the heart.

Speak Truth Affirmation: I have hope! God is doing all sorts of beautiful things in my head and heart. Regardless of what things look like in the world, I am confident of the future because God is on His throne! He has His hand on me and will not let me go. God has good things in store for me. My future is bright and sure! I am safe. I am protected. I have hope!

Speak Affirmation Support:
- *Surely there is a future, and your hope will not be cut off.* (Proverbs 23:18)
- *For I know the plans I have for you, declares the Lord, plans for welfare and not for evil, to give you a future and a hope.* (Jeremiah 29:11)
- *For by grace you have been saved through faith. And this is not your own doing; it is the gift of God...* (Ephesians 2:8)

4. TRUTH DROPS

Anoint: Apply 1-3 drops of Affirmation Oil #4 to the edges of each ear.

Speak Truth Affirmation: God is transforming the trials I've faced into assets for my ultimate good. I will push into the pain and watch it bear fruit. I will keep moving forward. He will not waste any of my pain and none of it comes close to comparing to the overwhelming joy to come. Because of Jesus, I am an overcomer. I am strong. I am steadfast. I am at peace.

Speak Affirmation Support:
- *Looking to Jesus, the founder and perfecter of our faith, who for the joy that was set before Him endured the cross, despising the shame, and is seated at the right hand of the throne of God.* (Hebrews 12:2)

- *I have said these things to you, that in Me you may have peace. In the world you will have tribulation. But take heart; I have overcome the world.* (John 16:33)
- *He gives power to the weak, and to those who have no might He increases strength.* (Isaiah 40:29)

5. TRUTH DROPS

Anoint: Apply 1-3 drops of Affirmation Oil #5 on the bottom of each foot.

Speak Truth Affirmation: I feel strong and sure! I have deep reserves of strength that come straight from my Father in Heaven. He supplies all that I need to move forward and thrive! I am calm and filled with self-value and joy. I am confident. I am patient. I am being renewed. I am energized!

Speak Affirmation Support:
- *Be strong and courageous. Do not be frightened, and do not be dismayed, for the Lord your God is with you wherever you go.* (Joshua 1:9)
- *But they who wait for the Lord shall renew their strength; they shall mount up with wings like eagles; they shall run and not be weary; they shall walk and not faint.* (Isaiah 40:31)
- *May the God of hope fill you with all joy and peace in believing, so that by the power of the Holy Spirit you may abound in hope.* (Romans 15:13)

JOURNAL PROMPT: What memories did God bring to your mind during this session? Write them down.

Ask the Lord to search you and reveal any toxic thoughts, memories, or trauma that He wants you to release to Him. Concentrate on becoming self-aware of your feelings and emotions: Anger? Shame? Sadness? Fear?

What emotions are you feeling? Where are you feeling them? When have you felt them before? Anoint yourself with your Prayer Oil by applying it directly to the place where you feel the emotion and ask the Lord to touch you—to heal you.

Ask God to also show you any bitterness or unforgiveness that you've harbored and forgive and release that, too.

Allow yourself to experience the pain or loss; but, this time, ponder the fact that Jesus was there with you the whole time, tenderly holding your soul and looking upon you with love and compassion, and looking ahead to your bright future.

How does that thought make you feel? Write out your experience and anything else the Lord shows you during this session. Pray and express your gratitude to God for what He is doing in you.

The Story of My Soul

A Picture of My Trauma and the Healing Power of Jesus

I am forsaken
Cold
Alone
Rejected
Forgotten
Broken
Condemned

Shame, my dearest enemy, stood over my paralyzed body. At times, I could see the threatening gleam of his dagger through the thick mist of confusion and self-reproach. His taunting serenade told stories of my past, as well as my hopeless fate. Tears burned my eyes as I held my breath and resigned myself to the inevitable. "I deserve it," I whispered. It was true. My own words hung in the air, mixing with the mist.

I wasn't sure if it was my heartbeat or the approaching footsteps that pounded in my head. My body trembled as a choking panic began to steal my breath. Wait! No! It couldn't be!

I was stunned. His eyes shot fire! Silence sliced through the air. A voice charged with holy authority and compassion thundered through the darkness, "She is Mine!"

It was all He said.

I laid there in silence, afraid to move. The mocking had suddenly ceased, as the light consumed the darkness. My eyes burned with tears. I gasped when I saw Him there, startled by the crimson puncture wounds in His feet.

I looked to see if my Enemy saw them, too. For a moment, I panicked—where had Shame gone? Then I saw it: The dagger in my own trembling hand. My head was spinning.

My Beloved reached out to me. The nail marks in His hands challenged and rebuked my doubts.

His tender eyes invited me to embrace boldly the providence of my past—the story of my soul. He reached out. I rose and took a small step toward Him, longing to walk in the freedom of my future—a freedom I knew was already mine—a freedom that had been paid for long, long ago.

Finally, I cast down the wretched dagger—my strange, familiar friend. As I gazed into the eyes of the Lover of my Soul, I remembered the blood stains on the blade with which I had for so long been tormented.

I gasped. All this time...all those years. The blood on the blade had been His—it was the blood He had shed—the blood that had already covered my shame the day I put my trust in Him. I was free.

The words He had spoken burned through my mind with a healing fire, searing their meaning into my soul: "She is Mine."

I am His
Safe
Wanted
Cherished
Found
Renewed
Redeemed

Thus says the Lord, who created you...and He who formed you... "Fear not, for I have redeemed you; I have called you by name; you are Mine." (Isaiah 43:1)

CONCLUSION
Practice Does Not Make Perfect

Not that I have already obtained this or am already perfect, but I press on to make it my own, because Christ Jesus has made me His own. (Philippians 3:12)

Ah…perfection! That ever-elusive goal. An important thing to remember is that in this life, we are healing; we are not yet healed. In a way, I think Christians often romanticize "getting saved," as if God is some sort of fairy godmother who touches us with his wand of salvation and Poof! All of our sinful habits and earthly troubles vanish in an instant!

The Christian experience is so much richer, deeper, and personal than that. Yes, in an instant, we *are* changed—we are new creations in Christ, but while on this earth, we will always have the flesh to contend with. When we become a Christian, it's not the end of the journey; it's only the beginning.

"O Shepherd. You said you would make my feet like hinds' feet and set me upon High Places."

"Well," he answered, "the only way to develop hinds' feet is to go by the paths which the hinds use."—*Hinds' Feet on High Places*, Hannah Hurnard

We don't suddenly love people better; but we are finally *free* to start (Romans 8:2). We don't suddenly lose all our old temptations to do the wrong thing; but our slavery to sin is finally over, and we are finally *free* to do the right thing. It can be a long, hard journey. Our desires slowly come into sync with Christ's desires. Sanctification is a process, and retraining our brain—our flesh—is an important and necessary part of it.

Use It or Lose It!

Don't forget, you will become good at whatever you put into practice (Deuteronomy 6:6-9). Paul said in Philippians 4:9, "What you have learned and received and heard and seen in me—*practice* these things, and the *God of peace will be with you*" [emphasis mine]. He didn't say "try hard to do these things" or "make this your goal;" he said, *practice* it!" And a few verses later, he expands his point: "I can do all things through Him who strengthens me." God has your back!

Have you ever seen a football player who no longer plays football—he stopped training and working out? Maybe he started to kick back and *watch* football instead of playing it. It shows in his body, his stamina, and his level of strength. He may gain weight, lose muscle tone, and tire easily.

Don't let this happen to your mind! Renewing the mind is a life-long process. Keep going. You've created some powerful new brain habits—new neural pathways have been formed that will help you steer clear of toxic thoughts and automatically redirect you to the truths of Scripture, so keep practicing! You are being made perfect.

> *Do not be conformed to this world, but be transformed by the renewal of your mind.* (Romans 12:2)

Which oils are you now most drawn to? Use your favorite emotion oils and blends to continue to maintain your progress and to preserve the healthy thoughts you've established.

Whether you've been dealing with simple past hurts, negative thought patterns, or working with a therapist through trauma from your past, you can continue to create and maintain new, healthier pathways in your brain. Leverage your limbic system each day by using essential oils and Scripture to keep your thoughts focused and moving in the right direction.

Remember our glorious hope! We can cling to the promise that, whatever loss we've endured, no matter the devastation, Jesus more than makes up for it. He fills all our voids to overflowing. When He ordains for us to endure suffering, we are assured it is temporary, and it in no way compares to the indescribable joy that is to come!

She had the feeling that somehow, in the very far-off places, perhaps even in far-off ages, there would be a meaning found to all sorrow and an answer too fair and wonderful to be as yet understood.
—Hannah Hurnard, *Hinds Feet on High Places*

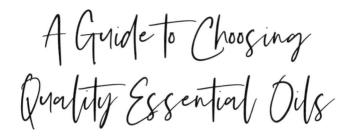
A Guide to Choosing Quality Essential Oils

To contact the author or access updated essential oil information and bundle suggestions, visit www.stacymcdonald.com.

Millions of people around the world have discovered the numerous benefits of God's gift of pure essential oils—oils carefully derived naturally from plants, trees, and flowers. Still, there are many copycat oils that are not fit for using on humans. In fact, some could even be dangerous.

It's important to use only the highest quality oils from a company that you are sure embraces a rigorous quality control standard that meets strict specifications in the following areas: Sourcing, Science, and Standards.

Whatever brand you choose, I suggest you do your own research first. The following standards are the non-negotiable benchmarks for selecting which oils I will put on or in my body (or even deliberately inhale).

SOURCING

Not all essential oils are created equal. It's crucial that you use oils only from a company you fully trust for purity and expertise—one that is committed to never adding synthetics, contaminants, or cheap fillers, or using unethical production practices.

Unfortunately, there are many companies out there who claim purity, but they are anything but pure or natural, so be careful. In fact, some companies sell oils that are adulterated with synthetic ingredients or contaminated during the growing or distillation process.

Many companies often use chemical solvents to extract a higher yield of oil from the plant, adulterating the final product by leaving behind traces of the chemical. When essential oils become more about profit than people, it's all about quantity, not quality.

Sometimes, essentials oils are contaminated before they even get to the distillation process. While the plants are still growing in the fields, their leaves are sprayed with pesticides, herbicides, or chemical-laced fertilizers. The plants may even be watered with chlorine-contaminated water.

Look for a company that only sources products from carefully vetted corporate-owned farms, partner farms, and company-certified suppliers, and make sure that they are grown on virgin soil and kept pure from the time they're planted in the ground until you receive the bottle in the mail.

Personally, knowing what I know, *Young Living*® is the only brand of essential oils I will use. I want oils that are not only pure, but that also work!

SCIENCE

Years ago, I had the privilege of hearing a fascinating lecture by brilliant essential oil pioneer and expert, Dr. Gary Young. He instructed us on the intricate process of growing, harvesting, and distilling essential oils without contaminating or destroying the delicate constituents in each individual oil.

He talked about the importance of temperature, pressure, and timing for each unique oil being distilled, what the pipes were made of, and the list goes on. There is just so much to know!

- When does each plant have the highest level of oil for distillation?
- How long should you leave the plants on the ground before distillation?
- Do you leave them in the sun or in the shade?
- Do you let them dry 10 hours or 24? A few days or a week?
- What temperature do you use? Get it wrong and you've destroyed important constituents.
- What pressure do you use?

All these points and more are crucial as the requirements are different for every single type of essential oil! Most people don't know this and think an essential oil is only about smelling good. Expertise is required to get good results—expertise most distillers do not have.

While you're doing your research, pay special attention to how the company distills and tests the oils they provide. Make sure they use extensive, in-house testing, as well as leverage leading, independent, and accredited labs with highly skilled and trained scientists who specialize in advanced product testing.

I truly believe that distillation is the most important step in the essential oil process—anyone can plant a plant, grow a plant, or harvest a plant, but distillation determines quality.—Dr. Gary Young

Testing should include these tests and more:
- Densitometry
- Viscometry
- Refractometry
- Olfactometry
- Polarimetry
- Inductively Coupled Plasma Mass Spectrometry (ICP-MS)
- Inductively Coupled Plasma-Atomic Optical Emission Spectrometry (ICP-OES)
- Gas Chromatography (GC)
- High Performance Liquid Chromatography (HPLC)
- Fourier Transform Infrared Spectroscopy
- Automated Micro-Enumeration
- Accelerated Stability Testing
- Disintegration
- pH
- Microscopy
- Combustibility
- Flash Point
- Water Activity
- Gas Chromatography Mass Spectrometry (GCMS)
- Chiral Chromatography
- Isotope Ratio Mass Spectrometry (IRMS)

STANDARDS

God gave us the earth and all that is in it to steward for Him, which means we need to nurture and protect our natural resources. Standards matter. For an essential oil company to make sure they aren't violating the planet by either unnecessarily polluting it or by ravaging endangered species of plants, it requires adherence to a higher standard of ethical behavior.

Recommended Essential Oils and Bundles

He made the holy anointing oil also, and the pure fragrant incense, blended as by the perfumer. (Exodus 37:29)

Please follow the application protocol as directed in each individual aromatherapy exercise.[24] Breathe deeply, as you reflect, meditate, and embrace the meaning of each Truth Drop Session, and internalize the reality of who God is and what He says about you.

SUGGESTED BUNDLES

Choose One Truth Drop Bundle or Create Your Own!

RESTORATION BUNDLE

I will restore to you the years that the swarming locust has eaten. (Joel 2:25)

Chosen Prayer Oil: Frankincense
Chosen Affirmation Oil #1: Inner Child™
Chosen Affirmation Oil #2: SARA™
Chosen Affirmation Oil #3: Petitgrain
Chosen Affirmation Oil #4: Release™
Chosen Affirmation Oil #5: Highest Potential™

---

24   *Disclaimer: The purpose of incorporating essential oils into this protocol is to help the reader learn to relax and create a mental habit of associating different aromas with the unwavering truth of God's Word. The aromatherapy sessions (Truth Drops) in this book are not intended to prescribe or treat any mental health condition or to replace professional therapy. If you believe you have a mental health disorder, please seek the help of a licensed mental health professional. Neither the author, publisher, nor Young Living® Essential Oils bear any responsibility for the misuse of this book or any of the products recommended.*

CONFIDENCE BUNDLE
Let us then with confidence draw near to the throne of grace... (Hebrews 4:16)
Chosen Prayer Oil: Sacred Sandalwood (Aloes)
Chosen Affirmation Oil #1: Motivation™
Chosen Affirmation Oil #2: Petitgrain
Chosen Affirmation Oil #3: Gratitude™
Chosen Affirmation Oil #4: Neroli
Chosen Affirmation Oil #5: Valor®

BODY IMAGE BUNDLE
I am fearfully and wonderfully made. Wonderful are Your works... (Psalm 139:14)
Chosen Prayer Oil: Rose of Sharon (Cistus)
Chosen Affirmation Oil #1: Vetiver
Chosen Affirmation Oil #2: Gratitude™
Chosen Affirmation Oil #3: Petitgrain
Chosen Affirmation Oil #4: White Angelica™
Chosen Affirmation Oil #5: Abundance™

SHAME BUNDLE
You will forget the shame of your youth... (Isaiah 54:4)
Chosen Prayer Oil: Hyssop
Chosen Affirmation Oil #1: Inner Child™
Chosen Affirmation Oil #2: Sacred Mountain™
Chosen Affirmation Oil #3: SARA™
Chosen Affirmation Oil #4: Release™
Chosen Affirmation Oil #5: Neroli

INNER JOY BUNDLE
Everlasting joy shall be upon their heads...sorrow and sighing shall flee away. (Isaiah 51:11)
Chosen Prayer Oil: Onycha
Chosen Affirmation Oil #1: Sacred Mountain™
Chosen Affirmation Oil #2: Present Time™
Chosen Affirmation Oil #3: Tranquil™
Chosen Affirmation Oil #4: Hope™
Chosen Affirmation Oil #5: Joy™

GLADNESS BUNDLE
The oil of gladness instead of mourning… (Isaiah 61:3)
    Chosen Prayer Oil: Frankincense
    Chosen Affirmation Oil #1: Orange
    Chosen Affirmation Oil #2: One Voice™
    Chosen Affirmation Oil #3: Peace & Calming™
    Chosen Affirmation Oil #4: Lavender
    Chosen Affirmation Oil #5: Joy™

FORGIVENESS BUNDLE
If the Son makes you free, you shall be free indeed. (John 8:36)
    Chosen Prayer Oil: Sacred Sandalwood
    Chosen Affirmation Oil #1: Inner Child™
    Chosen Affirmation Oil #2: Trauma life™
    Chosen Affirmation Oil #3: Forgiveness™
    Chosen Affirmation Oil #4: Surrender™
    Chosen Affirmation Oil #5: Release™

CONSOLATION & COMFORT BUNDLE
To console those who mourn in Zion, to give them beauty for ashes, the oil of joy for mourning, the garment of praise for the spirit of heaviness. (Isaiah 61:3, NKJV)
    Chosen Prayer Oil: Rose of Sharon (Cistus)
    Chosen Affirmation Oil #1: Present Time™
    Chosen Affirmation Oil #2: Hope™
    Chosen Affirmation Oil #3: Neroli
    Chosen Affirmation Oil #4: Gratitude™
    Chosen Affirmation Oil #5: Joy™

ABUNDANCE BUNDLE
But the meek shall inherit the earth and shall delight themselves in the abundance of peace. (Psalm 37:11)
    Chosen Prayer Oil: Frankincense
    Chosen Affirmation Oil #1: Motivation™
    Chosen Affirmation Oil #2: Envision™
    Chosen Affirmation Oil #3: Magnify Your Purpose™
    Chosen Affirmation Oil #4: Highest Potential™
    Chosen Affirmation Oil #5: Abundance™

ASSURANCE BUNDLE

I have come that they may have life, and that they may have it more abundantly.
(John 10:10)
    Chosen Prayer Oil: Cedarwood
    Chosen Affirmation Oil #1: Believe™
    Chosen Affirmation Oil #2: Petitgrain
    Chosen Affirmation Oil #3: Hope™
    Chosen Affirmation Oil #4: Gathering™
    Chosen Affirmation Oil #5: Valor®

CONNECTION BUNDLE

Two are better than one... (Ecclesiastes 4:9)
    Chosen Prayer Oil: Myrtle
    Chosen Affirmation Oil #1: Gathering™
    Chosen Affirmation Oil #2: Black Pepper
    Chosen Affirmation Oil #3: Sensation™
    Chosen Affirmation Oil #4: Transformation™
    Chosen Affirmation Oil #5: Awaken™

Whichever bundle you choose or create, be sure to use the same oil combination for the full nine weeks. However, when necessary, you may switch to a new bundle at the 30-day mark. This is particularly necessary if you are using the *Freedom Sleep*™ and *Release*™ *Collection*[25]:

FREEDOM BUNDLE[26]

He has sent me to proclaim liberty to the captives and recovering of sight to the blind, to set at liberty those who are oppressed. (Luke 4:18)

Freedom Sleep
Week 1-5
    Chosen Prayer Oil: Frankincense
    Chosen Affirmation Oil #1: Freedom™
    Chosen Affirmation Oil #2: AromaSleep™
    Chosen Affirmation Oil #3: Valor®
    Chosen Affirmation Oil #4: Inner Harmony™
    Chosen Affirmation Oil #5: Cedarwood

---

25   Young Living's *Freedom Sleep*™ *and Release*™ *Collection* comes with its own unique application instructions.
26   All but two of the oils in the Freedom Bundle (Frankincense and Cedarwood) are included in the *Freedom Sleep*™ and *Release*™ *Collection* sold as a set by *Young Living*®.

Freedom Release
Week 6-9

Chosen Prayer Oil: Frankincense
Chosen Affirmation Oil #1: Freedom™
Chosen Affirmation Oil #2: Joy™
Chosen Affirmation Oil #3: Transformation™
Chosen Affirmation Oil #4: Divine Release™
Chosen Affirmation Oil #5: T.R. Care™

SUGGESTED AFFIRMATION OILS

Singles
Bergamot
Copaiba
Geranium
Jasmine
Juniper
Lavender
Myrrh
Northern Lights Black Spruce
Petitgrain
Roman Chamomile
Rose
Spruce
Vetiver
Ylang Ylang

Blends
3 wise men™
Abundance™
Acceptance™
AromaEase™
Aroma Life™
Aroma Siez™
Australian Blue™
Awaken™
Believe™
Brain Power™
Calm™ (Seedlings®)
Celebration™

Chivalry™
Clarity™
Common Sense™
Divine Destiny Collection™
    (Contains Daily Divine™, I am
    Blessed™, and I am Creative™)
Dream Catcher™
Envision™
Forgiveness™
Freedom™
Gathering™
Gentle Baby™
Gratitude™
Grounding™
Harmony™
Higher Unity™
Highest Potential™
Hope™
Humility™
Inner Child™
Into the Future™
Journey On™
Joy™
Magnify Your Purpose™
Motivation™
One Heart™
One Voice™
Peace & Calming®
Present Time™

Release™   Tranquil ™
Rise Above™   Transformation™
Sacred Mountain™   Trauma Life™
Sara™   Valor®
Stress Away™   White Angelica™
Surrender™

SUGGESTED PRAYER OILS

Aloes (Sacred Sandalwood)
Cassia
Cedarwood
Cypress
Frankincense
Galbanum (endangered, currently unavailable)
Hyssop
Myrrh
Myrtle
Onycha
Rose of Sharon (Cistus)
Spikenard (endangered, currently unavailable)

SUGGESTED EMOTIONAL SUPPORT COLLECTIONS

Ancient Oils of Scripture™ Collection
Freedom Sleep™ and Release™ Collection
Feelings™ Collection
Divine Destiny™ Collection
Reconnect™ Collection

Recommended Reading:

Aromatherapy: The Essential Beginning by Dr. Gary Young
The Betrayal Bond: Breaking Free of Exploitive Relationships by Carnes PhD,
    Patrick
The Body Keeps the Score by Bessel Van Der Kolk, M.D.
The Body Remembers: The Psychophysiology of Trauma and Trauma Treatment
    by Babette Rothschild
The Bondage Breaker: Overcoming Negative Thoughts, Irrational Feelings, Habitual
    Sins by Neil Anderson
Boundaries for Your Soul: How to Turn Your Overwhelming Thoughts and Feelings
    into Your Greatest Allies by Allison Cook PhD
Boundaries: When to Say Yes, How to Say No to Take Control of Your Life
    by Henry Cloud and John Townsend
Breaking Emotional Barriers to Healing: Understanding the Mind-Body Connection
    to Your Illness by Craig A. Miller
Conquering Toxic Emotions by Rhonda Favano
The Emotionally Destructive Relationship: Seeing It, Stopping It, Surviving It
    by Leslie Vernick
Freedom from Fear by Neil Anderson
From Bondage to Bonding: Escaping Codependency, Embracing Biblical Love
    by Nancy Groom
Healing from Hidden Abuse: A Journey Through the Stages of Recovery from
    Psychological Abuse by Shannon Thomas, LCSW
Healing of Memories by David Seamands
Healing Oils of the Bible by Dr. David Stewart
How Do Essential Oils Work? by Dr. Doug Corrigan
Jesus & Me: A Journey of Love, Healing, and Freedom by Kimberly Weber
Practical Guide to Complex PTSD, A: Compassionate Strategies to Begin Healing
    from Childhood Trauma by Arielle Schwartz, PhD
Safe People: How to Find Relationships that are Good for You and Avoid Those That
    Aren't by Henry Cloud
Shame Interrupted by Edward T. Welch
Switch on Your Brain by Caroline Leaf